YANN ARTHUS-BERTRAND

2 DEGREES TOO HIGH

GoodPlanet.org

A book by GoodPlanet, a public interest foundation created by Yann Arthus-Bertrand.
Find out more about the foundation's activities and offer your support: www.goodplanet.org
To learn more about global warming and climate change negotiations: www.goodplanet.info
All royalties from book sales go to the foundation.

GoodPlanet chief editor: Olivier Blond.

Editorial staff: Alexandre Barbe, Olivier Blond, Cécile Cros, Jérémy Debreu, Anne Jankeliowitch, Marie-Thérèse Ménager, Julien Leprovost, Olivier Milhomme, Émilie Potard, Diana Semaska, Matthieu Tiberghien and Damien Urrutia.

Translation: Fredline Laryea.

Copyediting (English): Christopher Pitts.

Iconography: Isabelle Bruneau, Françoise Jacquot and Erwan Sourget.

Map and graphic adaptation: Laurent Blondel / Coredoc.

Graphic design and layout: Bruno Morini / Ami-images.

The photographs and quotes at the beginning of each chapter are taken from accounts that were gathered as part of *6 billion Others* project produced by the French Agency for Environment and Energy Management (Ademe). Over 500 interviews on global warming were carried out in 17 countries to make this film in partnership with the UN (IPCC, ISDR, UNEP, UN-Habitat, WMO). This documentary can be viewed for free on the internet: www.6milliardsdautres.org.

6 billion Others team: Véronique Algan, Sabrina Auteau, Véronique Beauducel, Julie Brones, Emmanuel Cappellin, Damien Chatard, Florent Gilard, Claire Guibert, Anne Guillaume, Judith Haussling, Chloé Henry-Biabaud, Galitt Kenan, Aurélie Miquel, Sibylle d'Orgeval, Solveig Risacher, Baptiste Rouget-Luchaire, Jean Sebastien Seguin, Mélanie de Segundo and Isabelle Vayron.

We particularly wish to thank the Intergovernmental Panel on Climate Change for supporting this book and the *6 billion Others* project for granting us permission to use and adapt several diagrams. A special thank you goes to Carola Saibante.

A CIP catalogue record for this book is available from the British Library.

YANN ARTHUS-BERTRAND

2 DEGREES TOO HIGH

GoodPlanet.org

ABRAMS

'BRINGING ECOLOGY
WITHIN THE HUMAN KIND'

GoodPlanet.org

In my travels, I have seen how beautiful the Earth is, but also how endangered it is. This is why I created the GoodPlanet foundation, which aims to raise the level of environmental awareness in today's society.

To reach as many people as possible, the foundation distributes educational posters in French schools, organizes green holiday camps for underprivileged youth and publishes a website on the environment. GoodPlanet also takes concrete action to reduce greenhouse gas emissions through its *Action Carbone* programme. The *6 billion Others* teams travelled the world to interview those who are already experiencing the effects of global warming. Extracts from these interviews can be found in this book.

The United Nations Climate Change Conference in Copenhagen is approaching. In the coming years, this summit will be a primary reference for crucial negotiations. For this reason, I wanted to provide more information for those who want to understand climate change – its origins and its consequences – and for those who want to know what they can do. This is the aim of this book. The texts and charts that have been included are based on the work of the Intergovernmental Panel on Climate Change, which consists of the top scientists doing research on the subject. Thanks to the findings of these scientists, we know that the global temperature will increase by a minimum 2°C over the next several decades. It is already too late to prevent that. But we can stop it from going higher. Citizens, companies, communities and governments have to consider all that is at stake. More importantly, we need to do something. Each person has to accept their share of the responsibility and act.

It is too late to be pessimistic.

Yann Arthus-Bertrand

FOREWORD

The Intergovernmental Panel on Climate Change (IPCC) has published four comprehensive reports on climate change as well as a large number of specialized reports that cover more specific aspects of the subject. Each of these documents has contributed to informing the public about the scientific realities of climate change and providing a basis for action at the national and international levels. The Fourth Assessment Report (AR4) has made a particularly strong impact; even the world leaders at the 2009 G8 Summit in L'Aquila, Italy, commented upon it. The summit's final communiqué stated, 'We reaffirm the importance of the work of the Intergovernmental Panel on Climate Change (IPCC) and notably of its Fourth Assessment Report, which constitutes the most comprehensive assessment of the science'. Not only has the AR4 provided information far beyond what was available in the Third Assessment Report (TAR), but a conscious decision was made to disseminate the findings of the report on a much wider scale than before.

Since my time as vice-chairman of the IPCC, from 1997 to 2002, it has been my personal belief that the organization has to be proactive in publicizing the findings of our assessment reports. However, all of us in the IPCC understand our limitations in communicating our message to the general public. It is in this regard that certain specially qualified partners can play an extremely valuable role. When such a partner happens to be as gifted as Mr Yann Arthus-Bertrand, clearly the power of the IPCC's message is multiplied several-fold. I have met many artists, musicians and photographers dedicated to protecting the environment, but never have I met anyone as talented and committed to the subject as Mr Arthus-Bertrand. In this regard, he is a unique resource for the IPCC and this book, which is based on the wealth of information contained in the AR4, is an example both of his talent as well as his sense of mission. I have had the privilege of viewing Mr Arthus-Bertrand's stunning photographs, which not only provide visual evidence of the beauty of this planet and the threats that we are imposing on it, but also speak like living beings. His book dealing with the findings of the AR4 is clearly a valuable work that will appeal to those who read it. And no doubt many will read it on the strength of the author's reputation alone. It is essential that scientific exercises such as the AR4 be presented in a manner that is appealing and aesthetically powerful.

This is precisely what Mr. Arthus-Bertrand has done. I am sure that this book will not only be read by a large number of people across the globe, but it will also find a prominent place on the shelves of distinguished scholars, decision makers and business and industry leaders so that it can be revisited from time to time as a resource of note.

R.K. Pachauri
Director General, The Energy and Resources Institute (TERI)
Chairman, Intergovernmental Panel on Climate Change (IPCC)

CONTENTS

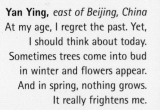

Yan Ying, *east of Beijing, China*
At my age, I regret the past. Yet,
I should think about today.
Sometimes trees come into bud
in winter and flowers appear.
And in spring, nothing grows.
It really frightens me.

Yan Ying

Abdul

Millie

Millie, *Northwest Territories, Canada*
Permafrost is melting – we know for sure. When you dig a grave, you find water
inside of it. It is one of the biggest changes I have witnessed. In the past, you used
to dig five or six feet deep and it was dry; now, there is water!
And you need to pump it out!

Abdul, *south of Dakha, Bangladesh*
Look, before we would have thirty, thirty-two years between a big storm and floods. Then we would have this kind of fear. Now, even before the year turns, we again have that storm, that flood, that change to bad weather. This climate is not changing back. Now this is how it is going on.

Nasira

Nasira, *Maldive Islands*
What has been changing in our life is that our island has been eroding and the trees keep falling due to erosion. When we were young, we used to play and swim on huge beaches. Now, we don't see that anymore.

HARBINGERS

Fay

Fay, *Northwest Territories, Canada*
In my house, the walls are starting to crack at the roof and the ceiling. It is going to fall apart sooner or later, but it still holds together. Permafrost is starting to melt and the house doesn't stay on the same level.

CLIMATE CHANGE

The weather has become a major issue in today's society. Up until recently it was no more than a subject for small talk, but now it is being debated at international summits by scientists, politicians, multinational companies and citizens. This is because the weather affects the lives of everyone.

'Natural' disasters are no longer considered natural, agricultural and industrial production is developing, and geostrategic relationships between nations have changed. The lifestyles of millions of people – and their possible forced displacement – are at stake, as is the transformation and even the disappearance of entire ecosystems. All of these things depend on the climate, a simple word that refers to a complex reality: air temperatures, cloud cover, pollution, ocean temperatures and currents, all measured over dozens of years.

But things change. Eleven out of the past twelve years have been the hottest on record since 1850. On average, surface temperatures around the world have increased by about 0.7 degrees Celsius over the past century. This does not seem like much; fluctuations in temperature from day to day and from hour to hour are often much more noticeable. However, it is actually quite significant, because the increase in average temperature is measured on a global scale. It is indicative of a profound transformation: we are not only dealing with global warming, but with global climate change.

This is only the beginning. Researchers estimate that temperatures will rise 2°C to 6°C by the end of the century. The rate and extent of the changes to come are still uncertain. However, the greatest uncertainty is no longer scientific, but political and social: will we be able to react quickly and effectively enough?

See also pages 34, 62 and 162.

> THE GREATEST UNCERTAINTY IS NO LONGER SCIENTIFIC, BUT POLITICAL AND SOCIAL: WILL WE BE ABLE TO REACT QUICKLY AND EFFECTIVELY ENOUGH?

San Rafael ice tongue, Chile (46°41'S, 73°50'W). In the sharp dusk light, the ice takes on a blue tint. Thirty thousand years old, the glacier finishes its journey as icebergs in the San Rafael Lagoon, which is connected to the Pacific Ocean. This is the closest glacier to the equator that reaches sea level. It has retreated about one kilometre over the past decade.

MELTING ICE

The majority of the Earth's glaciers are retreating; areas that were covered with ice last century are now bare. This is the most visible effect of global warming.

This phenomenon is caused by the dynamic nature of glaciers. Every summer, some of the ice disappears; every winter, new ice forms. Depending on whether there is more or less ice than the previous year, a glacier is either considered to be retreating (shrinking) or advancing (growing). A glacier's growth is directly related to air temperature. Because of global warming, glaciers around the world have retreated by an average of almost five hundred metres when compared to the beginning of the industrial era. They are not only retreating, but also becoming thinner. Over the past few years, glaciers have lost 230 billion tons of ice a year!

Antarctica and Greenland are particularly important because their icecaps contain 99 per cent of the Earth's ice. At the South Pole, the temperature drops to -70 °C in the winter, so the ice is not likely to disappear in the fore-

GLACIERS AROUND THE WORLD HAVE RETREATED BY AN AVERAGE OF ALMOST FIVE HUNDRED METRES WHEN COMPARED TO THE BEGINNING OF THE INDUSTRIAL ERA.

seeable future. But Antarctica is an immense continent with areas that are vastly different from each other. In some areas, snow cover is increasing slightly. In other areas, especially in the west (near Argentina and Chile), glaciers are melting. But, for the moment, global warming has not produced marked changes on the continent.

In Greenland, the situation is much more of a cause for concern. Until recently, researchers thought that the effects of global warming in Greenland would be moderate at worse. However, this has not proven to be the case. Over the past few years, Greenland's ice has been melting much faster than predicted.

The fate of glaciers and icecaps depends on greenhouse gases that are sometimes produced millions of miles away, in places like Paris, Beijing and Los Angeles. The changes in glaciers are indicative of the global nature of climatic warming. This global nature has created a new form of planetary responsibility.

See also pages 54, 56 and 68.

General view of Venice, Italy (45°25'N, 12°21'E). Venice is an archipelago made up of 118 islands, which are separated by 160 canals flowing beneath four hundred bridges. Because of sinking foundations, rising sea levels and increased flooding, it could one day disappear beneath the water. In 2002, the controversial project MOSE was adopted to block the inlets that link the sea to the lagoon, in case water levels rise.

RISING WATERS

Sea levels are rising. During the twentieth century they rose by an average of 1.7 millimetres a year, but the process is speeding up. Since the beginning of this century, sea levels have risen by an average of 3.1 millimetres a year.

There are two equally important reasons for this phenomenon. The first is that as the ocean warms up, it expands. The second is that as glaciers melt – in the Andes, the Himalayas and the Alps, for example – the water released eventually flows into the world's seas. Contrary to popular belief, melting ice floes at the poles are not actually a threat to coastlines, because the floes already displace the ocean water they float in. This paradox is called the ice-cube effect: if a glass containing a few ice cubes is filled to the brim, it will not overflow when the ice melts.

If moutain glaciers melt completely, however, they will make sea level rise by about fifty centimetres. But this is nothing when compared to what would happen if the ice caps in Greenland and Antarctica were to melt. Sea levels would rise by seven metres and fifty-six metres respectively!

A ONE CENTIMETRE INCREASE IN SEA LEVEL WILL CAUSE THE COASTLINE TO RECEDE BY ONE METRE.

Rising sea levels cause coastlines to recede by differing extents, depending on the topography. On average, a one centimetre increase in sea level will cause the coastline to recede by one metre, but it can be much more. In Louisiana, the coast has receded by almost one metre a year over the past few years. Another factor to take into account is that the ocean isn't flat. Warm and cold currents displace masses of water, causing seas to expand and contract, so some areas are several metres higher than others. Similarly, the increase in sea levels around the world is uneven.

The expansion of the world's oceans has a lot of inertia. It will take a long time to get started. It is expected to take at least a century for all of Greenland's ice to melt, if it happens. But this also means that once the phenomenon gets started, it will be hard to slow down. Even if we stop producing greenhouse effect gases, sea levels will continue to rise for a long time. We must therefore anticipate the problem.

See also pages 52, 68 and 76.

Ice tongue near the summit of Khan Tengri, Sary-Jaz Mountains, Issyk Kul Province, Kyrgyzstan (42°10'N, 80°00'E). Kyrgyzstan has numerous glaciers that effectively constitute the planet's water towers. The effects of global warming can even be felt here in Central Asia, where some of the world's highest mountains are found. It is possible that some mountain lakes could overflow and flood the inhabited valleys downstream.

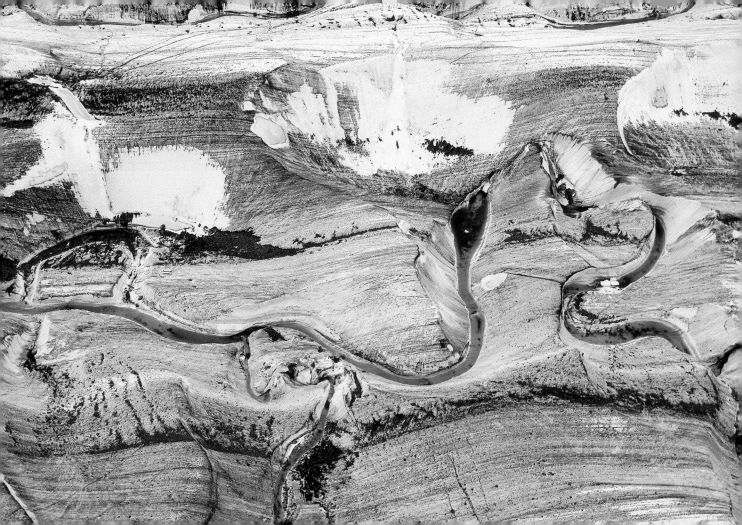

NATURAL DISASTERS

Two major natural disasters thrust climate change into the centre of public debate: the European heat wave in 2003 and Hurricane Katrina in 2005. The first resulted in almost thirty thousand deaths across Europe, nearly half of which were in France. The second caused over eighteen hundred fatalities and billions of dollars in damage in the United States. Other examples of extreme weather also occurred at the beginning of the twenty-first century, like disastrous floods in Central Europe and India, which caused dozens of deaths in 2005, and severe droughts in Australia, which resulted in forest fires.

It is hard to establish a clear link between these events and climate change; droughts, floods and storms have always existed. However, the series of natural catastrophes in the past few years has revealed certain trends. These trends indicate that the daily weather forecast – today or tomorrow's weather – has not changed. However, the overall climate – the average weather today and in years to come – has changed.

WE OFTEN TALK ABOUT CLIMATE CHANGE RATHER THAN GLOBAL WARMING.

Today, researchers estimate that global warming is increasing the probability of extreme weather. These different natural disasters have shown that the overall climate is not only warming up, but has also been disrupted. Depending on the region, this disruption can take on various forms: more rain in one place and less in another, more heat here and less elsewhere. To take into account the diversity of weather-related changes, we often talk about climate change rather than global warming.

In any event, no disaster is completely natural: heat waves and hurricanes are meteorological phenomena, but their consequences are even more dramatic because people have not always adequately prepared for them. In France there were not enough air-conditioned shelters, for example, and in New Orleans the levees were not well maintained. By anticipating future changes, we can reduce the impact of extreme weather.

See also pages 68, 78 and 84.

New Orleans after Hurricane Katrina, Louisiana, United States (30°00'N, 90°05'W). On August 29, 2005, Hurricane Katrina slammed into the Gulf Coast of the United States. Winds blowing at over two hundred kilometres per hour created powerful waves that breached the city's levees and flooded over 80 per cent of the city. Tens of thousands of residents were unable to leave the city and over one thousand people died.

DROUGHTS

Global warming is best defined as an increase in the average temperature at the Earth's surface. One of the most visible consequences of global warming is the change in types of precipitation. Evaporation over the oceans and continents is increasing. Because the atmosphere is warmer, it can also hold more water vapour, which results in more abundant and intense rainfall. We are heading towards a more humid world, with more precipitation.

But a hotter, more unstable climate also goes hand in hand with an increased frequency in extreme events, like floods and droughts, regardless of latitude. Recurring droughts could make agriculture impossible on land that is currently cultivated, like the Murray-Darling Basin in Australia. The causes of these disasters, however, are not all climate related. The development of riverbeds and drainage basins, combined with deforestation and the overuse of water tables, are also factors that aggravate such phenomena.

Even in areas where the overall rate of precipitation has not increased by much, if the distribution throughout the year varies, it could create recurring disasters. In a Mediterranean climate, for example, summer droughts could begin at the end of spring and last until autumn, while increased winter rains could cause erosion and flooding. In mountainous regions, a smaller proportion of precipitation is falling as snow; yet one-sixth of humanity depends on the water released by this snow when it melts. The flow of rivers is thus changing.

In other places, water levels are also decreasing. This is the case in subtropical regions in the northern hemisphere, where precipitation has fallen by 10 per cent since 1990. The surface area of regions subjected to extreme droughts, like the Sahel in Africa during the 1970s and 1980s, could increase ten- to thirty-fold. Up to 30 per cent of the world's regions will experience such phenomena before the end of the century, compared to just 1 to 3 percent today.

See also pages 24, 72 and 80.

> **RECURRING DROUGHTS COULD MAKE AGRICULTURE IMPOSSIBLE ON LAND THAT IS CURRENTLY CULTIVATED.**

Kebili Oasis, Nefzaoua, Tunisia (33°42′N, 8°58′E). Kebili is the main oasis in Nefzaoua, South Tunisia. This fertile area is surrounded by sand and irrigated with groundwater. However, the water table is drying up. The desert is not advancing; rather, the steppe is being degraded by human activity. Abandoned areas have been invaded by small wind-blown sand dunes.

ANIMALS ON THE FRONT LINE

Before human beings were even aware of climate change, animals and plants had already felt the first effects. Spring came earlier, and a milder climate allowed species to enter new regions. The time and space of the living world changed.

To find the conditions that best suit them, living organisms are now migrating towards cooler areas, either higher into the mountains or closer to the poles. In North America, the tundra vegetation is slowly being replaced by taiga plants, like conifers. Every year, the border between the two ecosystems moves northwards by an average of twelve kilometres. Insects everywhere take advantage of milder winters to widen their proliferation area. This is the case of the pine processionary, a caterpillar in Europe, and the mountain pine beetle, which is threatening millions of hectares of forest in Canada.

Even ocean life is affected: plankton in the Atlantic Ocean have moved northwards ten degrees in latitude – one thousand kilometres – over the past forty years! Such changes also affect humans. The change in plankton communities in the North Sea has severely reduced the number of cod, a fish that is an important resource for fisheries.

IF THE ARCTIC ICE COVER MELTS, POLAR BEARS WILL DISAPPEAR. THEY HAVE BECOME THE UNWILLING SYMBOLS OF GLOBAL WARMING AND ITS DANGERS.

Some species, like the polar bear, cannot escape. In winter, polar bears use ice floes as a platform from which to hunt and build up fat for the summer fast. But each decade the spring thaw has moved forward eight days, and the polar bear's hunting season has gotten shorter, while its fasting period has increased. In Canada's Hudson Bay, the number of polar bears has decreased by 22 per cent since 1987. The bears have become also thinner: on average, the females weigh seventy kilos less than thirty years ago. If the Arctic ice cover melts, polar bears will disappear. They have become the unwilling symbols of global warming and its dangers.

See also pages 74, 76 and 118.

Giraffes, Masai Mara National Reserve, Kenya (1°15′S, 35°15′E). Together with the Serengeti National Park in Tanzania, the Masai Mara is one of the largest protected areas in the world, covering twenty-five thousand square kilometres. It is known for the spectacular yearly migration of almost two million wildebeest. For about fifteen years the populations of certain herbivores, like giraffes, have been decreasing, particularly because of territorial conflicts with people.

A DIFFERENT TYPE OF AGRICULTURE

Farmers observe climate change first hand. They see the spring warmth arrive earlier and the autumn frosts come later. They see how plants bud, leaves open and vegetation grows earlier. In Europe, North America and Japan, flowers bloom nine days earlier than they did thirty years ago. On some French farms, corn can be sown twenty days earlier compared with thirty years ago.

How does this affect yields? Global warming is good news for wine producers. In Alsace, for example, the number of days that favour vine growth (when the average temperature is higher than 10°C) has increased from 170 in 1970 to 210 in 2000. In Europe and the United States, wine has become more stable and its quality has improved. For forestry, the growth of forests has increased from 6 to 12 per cent over the past two decades, depending on the region. This is not only because temperatures are warmer, but also because the increased carbon dioxide concentration has a direct positive effect on vegetation growth.

But this is not the case for all crops. Sometimes, a one-degree increase is enough to reduce the yield of paddy fields by 15 per cent, as has been observed in the Philippines. In countries that are already affected by drought, the increase in temperature combined with a decrease in rain means local agriculture is no longer possible. Peanuts, for example, are traditionally grown in Sahelian countries where it is a staple, but production is decreasing.

Up until now, the effects of global warming have been slight and difficult to pinpoint, especially when taking into account the significant changes in agriculture in the past decades. These changes have been driven by mechanisation, chemistry and biotechnology. However, as the increase in yields is slowing down and global warming is increasing, the situation could change.

See also pages 46, 72 and 108.

> ON SOME FRENCH FARMS, CORN CAN BE SOWN TWENTY DAYS EARLIER COMPARED WITH THIRTY YEARS AGO.

Cherry trees in the Bessenay Region, Rhône, France (45°46'N, 4°33'E). West of Lyon, four hundred hectares of cherry trees are growing in magnesium-rich soil at an altitude of three hundred to seven hundred metres. The fruit, which ripens in June and July, add three thousand tons to regional production. This region is the second-largest French producer of cherries, with an annual harvest of 21,850 tons.

OCEAN ACIDIFICATION

The increase in carbon-dioxide levels in the atmosphere has led to a chemical change in oceans, with consequences that are often neglected. Not only are the world's oceans getting warmer, they are also absorbing gases, like carbon dioxide, from the atmosphere. And because they cover 71 per cent of the Earth's surface area, they absorb large amounts of it: almost half of the carbon dioxide emitted into the atmosphere since the beginning of the Industrial Revolution in the eighteenth century has been absorbed by oceans.

The more carbon dioxide there is in the atmosphere, the more there is in the oceans. This affects the cellular metabolism of all types of marine life: when CO_2 reacts with water, the excess gas turns into carbonic acid. The acidity of seawater has increased by 30 per cent since the beginning of the Industrial Revolution.

The danger is not that seawater could become acidic. Ocean pH has always been higher than 7 – the neutral value – and there is plenty of leeway before it drops below

THE ACIDITY OF SEAWATER HAS INCREASED BY 30 PER CENT SINCE THE BEGINNING OF THE INDUSTRIAL REVOLUTION.

this. The problem is that many marine organisms that have a skeleton or shell are having a harder time calcifying. Because of acidification, it is harder for them to extract the minerals they need from the surrounding environment.

The entire ocean food chain – from phytoplankton, zooplankton, molluscs and starfish to crab to coral – has been affected. According to researchers, the phenomenon is going to get worse, and several species may disappear, which would disrupt marine ecosystems. Indeed, plankton photosynthesise; even though they only represent less than 1 per cent of the planet's biomass, they absorb almost as much carbon dioxide and produce as much oxygen as all vegetation on land. Acidification adds to global warming. Higher water temperatures also bleach coral reefs, which provide food and shelter for one-quarter of all marine species, and ultimately result in their death.

See also pages 48 and 52.

Nuami Islet, atoll of Nokan Hui, New Caledonia, France (22°45'S, 167°34'E). The Nuami Islet is the largest surface area in the atoll. In tropical seas, coral needs specific levels of heat, light and water quality to survive. If acidification or global warming change just one of these parameters, coral could perish.

SCEPTICS

What if this is all just a bad joke? An invention by scientists who want to frighten people and obtain funding for expensive studies? Some people claim this is the case, although their numbers are dwindling. They call themselves 'sceptics'; one of the most famous is the Danish economist Bjorn Lomborg, who wrote *The Skeptical Environmentalist*, published in 1998.

They are a diverse group of people who don't always agree. Some of them are recognised scientists; others know little about the subject. In the United States, the most important sceptics have been heavily subsidised by oil companies who have an obvious interest in the matter; Exxon, for example, has given them millions of dollars. This support has allowed sceptics to organize into extremely influential lobbies. Even today, it allows them to get disproportionate media coverage. They have played an important role in political debate and the government's attitude, especially in the United States.

Sceptics usually focus on uncertainties or minute mistakes in the details that are then used to question general data. The facts have indeed only been revealed progressively. A few decades ago, we were expecting future glaciation. But today, the debate is over. Over the past twenty years, thousands of researchers from over 130 countries – almost all specialists – have rallied around a branch of the United Nations, the Intergovernmental Panel of Climate Change (IPCC).

Many details still need to be clarified and many questions must still be answered. But thanks to the work of the IPCC, which was awarded the 2007 Nobel Peace Prize, there is no longer any doubt about the existence of global warming or its root cause: greenhouse gases emitted by human activity.

See also pages 50 and 62.

OVER THE PAST TWENTY YEARS, THOUSANDS OF RESEARCHERS FROM OVER 130 COUNTRIES – ALMOST ALL SPECIALISTS – HAVE RALLIED TOGETHER.

Waste from the copper mine at Chuquicamata, Chile (22°17′S, 68°52′W). This giant scallop is made of earth. A crane deposits the earth, which was separated from the copper by sieving, in successive, slightly curved lines. The copper is refined in the Chuquicamata foundry. Thanks to newly installed equipment, the foundry can now filter 95 per cent of the sulfur dioxide (SO_2) and 97 per cent of the arsenic it releases.

WHAT HAS ALREADY CHANGED

Climate change is no longer a hypothesis, it is a fact. Numerous scientific studies, represented by the dots on this map, show this to be true: our planet has already changed.

These changes are as varied as the world itself. In some cases temperatures are decreasing, but this does not call into question the general warming trend.

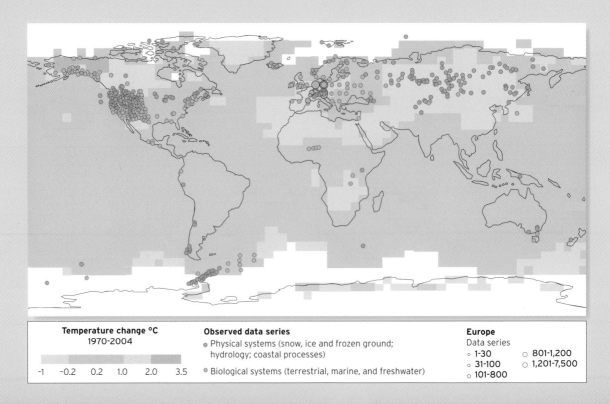

Temperature change °C
1970-2004

-1   -0.2   0.2   1.0   2.0   3.5

Observed data series

● Physical systems (snow, ice and frozen ground; hydrology; coastal processes)

● Biological systems (terrestrial, marine, and freshwater)

Europe
Data series
○ 1-30   ○ 801-1,200
○ 31-100   ○ 1,201-7,500
○ 101-800

A TREND THAT IS BECOMING CLEARER

Two of the planet's major parameters – the surface temperature and the sea level – have clearly changed over the past decades. Between 1905 and 2006, the planet's average temperature increased by 0.74°C. From 1961 to 1992, the average sea level increased by 1.8 millimetres a year. Since 1993, it has been increasing by 3.1 millimetres a year.

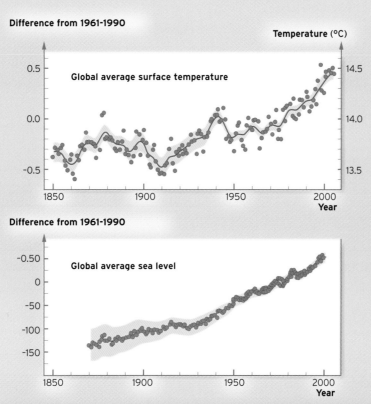

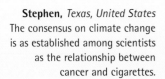

Stephen, *Texas, United States*
The consensus on climate change is as established among scientists as the relationship between cancer and cigarettes.

Stephen

Fay

Louis

Louis, *south of Spain*
According to scientific predictions, it is a disaster. It is not only one disaster, but a lot of them happening at the same time.

ay, *Northwest Territories, Canada*
...e are all responsible, even in the Arctic. For instance, here in Tuk, flying
...s the only way to leave town for nine months of the year if you need to see
...doctor, attend a meeting or go on a short trip. Our food also comes from
...he south by plane. And those who own a car leave the engine running
...ll day because they are afraid their car won't start again.

Vince, *Northwest Territories, Canada*
Coastal erosion has rapidly increased over the last ten years.
I think it is because of climate change. If winters are shorter,
it means less ice and more water movement on land; waves
break on the shore and cause erosion faster
than they used to. It is a big change.

Vince

MECHANISMS

Gloria, *China*
I don't know if climate change is natural or if it is a consequence
of human destruction. I am not a scientist; I have never studied these phenomena.
However, I think that the increase in population and the rise of industrialisation
must have some influence on climate change.
Humankind and nature are as one.

Gloria

THE GREENHOUSE EFFECT

Without the greenhouse effect, there would be no life on Earth. Not, in any case, life as we know it. The average temperature would be about -18°C, or perhaps even lower. It is currently about 15°C. This completely natural phenomenon is what allows us to exist. How? The sun's heat is largely absorbed by the Earth, but a fraction is sent back into the atmosphere as infrared rays. Greenhouse gases intercept these rays and reflect some of them back towards the Earth, helping to keep the surface warm. This is the greenhouse effect.

THERE IS A DIRECT RELATIONSHIP BETWEEN THE INTENSITY OF THE GREENHOUSE EFFECT AND THE AIR TEMPERATURE: THE MORE GAS THERE IS, THE HOTTER IT GETS.

 There is a direct relationship between the intensity of the greenhouse effect and the air temperature: the more gas there is, the hotter it gets. For example, on Venus the atmosphere contains many powerful gases; the temperature there is 460°C. Scientists have long been aware of this relationship. As early as 1896, the Swedish researcher Svante Arrhenius calculated that double the amount of CO_2 in the atmosphere would increase the planet's average temperature by 4°C. This relationship has since been confirmed and is now better understood.

Humans have an influence on the greenhouse effect. The amount of CO_2 in the atmosphere is measured in parts-per-million (ppm). Up until the Industrial Revolution in the eighteenth century, this figure was stable at around 270 ppm. Human activity has since generated a lot of emissions. In less than three centuries, the concentration of CO_2 has increased by about 30 per cent; it reached 387 ppm in 2008. The study of ice cores in Antarctica shows that it has not been this high in the past 650,000 years.

 Because greenhouse gas emissions linked to human activity are the main cause of climate change, they must be limited. This is the main issue that is debated during international negotiations, and, in particular, at the UN Climate Change Conference in Copenhagen.

See also pages 36, 50 and 62.

Icebergs off the coast of Adélie Land, Antarctica (67°00'S, 139°00'E). The study of trapped air bubbles in ice cores is a particularly important tool to understanding the sources of current climate change. The European EPICA program was launched to analyze deep ice cores in Antarctica. The researchers reached a drilling depth of 3,270 metres, which represents 800,000 years of climate archives.

GREENHOUSE GASES

Water vapour, a harmless molecule, is the most abundant greenhouse gas. Human activities only have a slight effect on the amount of water vapour present in the atmosphere. Thus, it only plays a secondary role in current global warming. However, the concentration of other greenhouse gases has increased significantly since the Industrial Revolution. These gases are carbon dioxide (CO_2), methane (CH_4), nitrous oxide (N_2O) and a group of rare gases, including halogen gases.

Paradoxically, CO_2 is one of the weakest greenhouse gases. A sulfur hexafluoride (SF_6) molecule, for example, is several thousand times more powerful than a CO_2 molecule. It also has a lifespan in the atmosphere of about 3,200 years, compared with one hundred years for CO_2. By combining these two parameters, researchers have calculated that over the course of a century, SF_6 has a Global Warming Potential (GWP) that is 22,800 times higher than CO_2! Luckily, only very small amounts of SF_6 are emitted into the atmosphere. In comparison, man emits about thirty billion tons of CO_2 annually.

IN 2004 CARBON DIOXIDE REPRESENTED 77 PER CENT OF GREENHOUSE GAS EMISSIONS LINKED TO HUMAN ACTIVITY.

The relative importance of different gases can be compared. In 2004 carbon dioxide represented 76.7 per cent of greenhouse gas emissions linked to human activity, methane represented 14.3 per cent, nitrous oxide 7.9 per cent, and halogen gases 1.1 per cent. CO_2 mainly comes from the combustion of fossil fuels and deforestation, while methane is mainly produced through agriculture and the use of natural gas. Nitrous oxide comes from fertilization and halogen gases are used in industry. Some are used as refrigerants and also weaken the ozone layer.

Each gas is emitted into the atmosphere by a different process. To limit these emissions, specific solutions – economic, technological and political – must be developed for each case.

See also pages 44, 50 and 62.

Posco electric steel mill in Gwangyang, South Korea, (34°55'N, 127°45'E). In an electric steel mill, steel is made from scrap iron that has been melted using electricity. The combustion of these raw materials from different sources is a cause of severe pollution in the atmosphere. Only small amounts of heavy metals (cadmium, lead, mercury) are emitted, but they accumulate in the soil and eventually enter the food chain.

FOSSIL FUELS

Oil is concentrated potential energy. One litre of oil is the equivalent of several weeks' worth of physical labour. With oil, one can propel a ton of metal (e.g. a car) dozens of kilometres. The downside to using this concentrated energy is the release of greenhouse gases. Burning one litre of oil releases 2.7 kilograms of CO_2 into the atmosphere, as well as other pollutants such as carbon monoxide, nitrogen oxides, sulphates and particles.

Our society consumes enormous amounts of energy and has become dependent on fossil fuels: oil, gas and coal represent 81 per cent of our primary energy consumption. Almost all economic activity and all products that are made, exchanged and consumed in the world rely on fossil fuels. The Gross Domestic Product (GDP) and greenhouse gas emissions are now following the same upward curve. Lately, this relationship has changed slightly because of improved energy efficiency and the development of renewable energy.

THE END OF OIL THAT IS OFTEN TALKED ABOUT WILL NOT SOLVE THE PROBLEM. IT COULD EVEN MAKE THINGS WORSE.

The end of oil that is often talked about will not solve the problem. It could even make things worse. Indeed, even the little oil that is left is enough to dangerously warm up our atmosphere. But, more important than oil is coal, which could take over as our primary energy source. It is estimated that at the current rate of consumption, coal reserves will last for another 150 years. In spite of its old-fashioned image, it is already widely used in power plants all over the world. In China, for example, a new coal-fired power plant opens every week! It is even possible to turn it into petrol. This process, which is used in South Africa, is highly pollutive.

Coal releases more CO_2 than gas or oil per unit of energy produced. It accounts for a quarter of world energy consumption, but it is responsible for 42 per cent of energy-related CO_2 emissions. If current trends continue, demand could double before 2030.

See also pages 92, 98 and 116.

Open-pit coal mine, Arizona, United States, (32°21'N, 111°12'W). The Kayenta Mine, near the heart of a Navajo Indian reservation in the southwest of the United States, is the last active strip mine in Arizona. Every year, machines extract over one billion metric tons of coal from 1,400 American mines. This makes the United States the second-largest coal producer after China.

THE ROLE OF TRANSPORTATION

The most significant increase in greenhouse gas emissions has been in the transportation sector: emissions have increased by 120 per cent between 1970 and 2004. There are several reasons for this. The expansion of the global market has increased the movements of goods and people. Part of the population has become richer – especially in developing countries – which has made it possible for more people to buy motorized vehicles. Mass tourism is constantly growing and urban sprawl is increasing our daily transportation.

Ninety-five per cent of vehicles in the world are powered by oil. Because engines emit large amounts of CO_2, transportation is responsible for a significant part of greenhouse gas emissions. Most of these emissions are caused by human transportation; almost half is caused by cars.

Technological progress may have made it possible to improve the energy efficiency of transportation, but the full potential was never realized. Car engines are usually

> TO GO FROM PARIS TO MARSEILLE, A JOURNEY OF 750 KILOMETRES, A PERSON EMITS ABOUT SIX KILOGRAMS OF CO_2 BY TRAIN COMPARED WITH THIRTY-FIVE KILOGRAMS BY CAR AND FIFTY KILOGRAMS BY PLANE.

more efficient than they were a few decades ago, but this improvement is offset by the increase in the average size and number of cars. With growing car travel, greenhouse gas emissions are currently increasing by 2 per cent a year on average.

All means of transportation are not equal. Some emit more greenhouse gases than others. To go from Paris to Marseille, a journey of about 750 kilometres, a person emits about six kilograms of CO_2 by train compared with thirty-five kilograms by car and fifty kilograms by plane. And almost none by bicycle – but this would definitely take much longer. In our speed-based society, the fastest means of transport are deemed to be the best, even though they use more energy. Those who can afford it upgrade from bicycles to motorcycles and from cars to planes. Air travel increases by 5 per cent a year – more than any other type of transportation.

See also pages 58, 106 and 156.

Motorway interchange near the Yokohama Port, Japan (35°27'N, 139°41'E). The motorways around the port are a symbol of economic development largely based on the ground transportation that complements container shipping. Yokohama used to be a fishing village. It is now the largest Japanese port and the country's second-largest city. There are nearly one billion cars on Earth.

THE ROLE OF CITIES

The temperature in cities is always warmer by 2°C on average; sometimes, it is even higher than that. This is not just because of the concentration of human activity, but also because of the way cities are built: the asphalt, the large buildings and so on. However, this is not why cities are contributing to global warming.

The main factor is energy consumption, especially in buildings. This alone accounts for almost 8 per cent of the world's human-related greenhouse gas emissions. In countries like the United States, one-third of these emissions are linked to heating in winter and cooling in summer. Air conditioners make the problem they are supposed to be solving three times worse. They consume enormous amounts of energy and are therefore responsible for greenhouse gas emissions. They also emit hot air and use powerful greenhouse gases for cooling.

Indoor and outdoor lighting is responsible for the emission of 1.9 billion tons of CO_2 every year. This figure could be considerably reduced with new energy-saving bulbs. In a country like France, refrigerators and freezers consume one-third of total electricity consumption while lighting and audiovisual equipment consumes one-fourth.

Higher standards of living, larger populations and the increase in the number and size of houses mean that more energy is needed. The tertiarisation of the economy also plays a big role as services, trade and information technology require large amounts of energy.

But, paradoxically, the high population density in cities helps to save energy. Buildings are usually easier to heat and better insulated than houses. The latter need their own roads, piping and electricity cables, which requires the reuse of energy and building materials for each individual house.

See also pages 106, 120 and 184.

PARADOXICALLY, THE HIGH POPULATION DENSITY IN CITIES HELPS TO SAVE ENERGY.

La Cité du Lignon, Geneva, Switzerland (46°12'N, 6°05'E). La cité du Lignon, built in 1962, is made up of 2,780 apartments and is home to over 5,500 people. In Geneva, rapid population growth and a property boom have resulted in many people having to move to the suburbs. This increases the number of peri-urban journeys. Every year, 2,100 hectares of natural space is sacrificed for urbanisation. Half of this is used just for housing.

CARBON SINKS

Fortunately, nature helps humans. Over the past century, we have emitted billions of tons of carbon into the atmosphere, but only some of it – 43 per cent – has really contributed to increasing the greenhouse effect. The rest was absorbed by oceans, forests and soil. Carbon is said to be trapped, stocked or even held when it does not – provisionally – return to the atmosphere. This is why forests and oceans are also referred to as 'carbon sinks'.

Trees and vegetation usually absorb CO_2 in the atmosphere through photosynthesis. They turn the gas into living matter and release oxygen: this is the carbon cycle. But oceans are the main natural carbon sinks. Here again, the chain starts with photosynthesis: algae absorb CO_2 in the same way as other plants. Some species of phytoplankton also use it for calcification in order to build their skeletons or shells.

TERRESTRIAL SYSTEMS STORE THREE TIMES THE AMOUNT OF CARBON CURRENTLY PRESENT IN THE ATMOSPHERE.

It is still difficult to estimate the amount of CO_2 these natural sinks store. Taking them into account as measures against global warming is also very delicate. However, this is an important issue as terrestrial systems – forests, soil, grasslands and wetlands – store three times the amount of carbon currently present in the atmosphere.

But this natural mechanism is almost at a breaking point. The current temperature increase is slowing photosynthesis down. The 2003 European heat wave disrupted it momentarily. Additionally, the temperature increase and acidification of oceans may disrupt biodiversity and absorption capacity; the sinks could become 'sources'. This means that they could emit some of their carbon stores and intensify the phenomenon they previously regulated.

See also pages 46, 110 and 154.

Storm over the Amazon Forest near Tefè, Amazonas, Brazil (3°32'S, 64°53'W). Covering an area of 3.7 million square kilometres, the Amazon is the world's largest tropical forest ecosystem. It accounts for one-third of the planet's tropical forests and is home to about one-half of the Earth's species. Every day, almost two hundred square kilometres of forest are cut down around the world, taking the secrets of many unknown species with them.

AGRICULTURE

Humans do not only burn oil. We also burn forests. Today, deforestation is responsible for one-third of all human-related CO_2 emissions. Cutting trees releases the carbon they store. It also changes the makeup of the soil, which sometimes contains even more carbon than on the surface. In Indonesia, the destruction of peat bogs to make room for palm tree plantations has made the country the third-highest CO_2 emitter.

Agriculture is a factory that produces greenhouse gases. It is the main source of methane and nitrous oxide emissions. These two greenhouse gases contribute the most to the greenhouse effect after carbon dioxide. Over a one-hundred-year span, the global-warming potential of methane is twenty-five times stronger than CO_2, while the global-warming potential of nitrous oxide is 298 times stronger. Rice cultivation, for example, releases large amounts of methane. Growing one kilo of rice emits an average of 120 grams. This means that rice growing produces sixty million tons of methane every year. The use of synthetic fertilizers is the main source of nitrous oxide.

GROWING ONE KILO OF RICE EMITS AN AVERAGE OF 120 GRAMS OF METHANE, WHICH MAKES SIXTY MILLION TONS PER YEAR.

Cattle farming is also responsible for many emissions. It indirectly causes deforestation: either to make room for pastures or to grow soya beans for cattle feed. Additionally, cattle produce methane in their digestive system, which they emit – about eighty million tons a year – through burping or flatulence. In total, livestock farming is responsible for about 18 percent of all greenhouse gas emissions – more than transportation!

Unfortunately, the idyllic image of small farmers living in harmony with nature no longer reflects the reality of most developed countries. Large farms use chemically produced fertilizers and pesticides as well as machines that need fuel. It is our entire society that produces greenhouse gases, not just power plants and factories.

See also pages 24, 72 and 108.

Deforestation for oil palm plantations near Pundu, Borneo, Indonesia (1°59'S, 113°06'E). On the island of Borneo, oil palm plantations are replacing virgin tropical forests. These plantations result in the loss of 80 per cent of original plant life and 80 to 90 per cent of native animal species like the orang-utan. Global demand for palm oil (used to make food products, detergents and cosmetics) is the main cause of deforestation in Indonesia.

VICIOUS CIRCLES

Vicious circles are referred to in science as 'positive feedback'. This means that once a phenomenon has begun, it will increase or speed up its own development. In the global warming process, at least three examples of this effect have been identified.

The first is melting ice in the Arctic. With regard to sunlight, ice is the most reflective surface; water is the most absorptive surface. When an ice floe melts, the area that used to reflect the sun's heat now begins to absorb it. Thus, the more an ice floe melts, the more the area warms up; eventually, the floe melts entirely. This partially explains why the warming observed at high latitudes is about twice as intense as on average.

Another example is permafrost, soil that is frozen year round. When permafrost melts it releases methane, a greenhouse gas that is twenty-five times stronger than CO_2. This speeds up the greenhouse effect and, therefore, global warming. This effect could further

WHEN PERMAFROST MELTS
IT RELEASES METHANE,
A GREENHOUSE GAS THAT IS TWENTY-
FIVE TIMES STRONGER THAN CO_2. THIS
SPEEDS UP THE GREENHOUSE EFFECT
AND, THEREFORE, GLOBAL WARMING.

speed up if the methane that ice has trapped on the ocean floor is also released. This phenomenon could take on disastrous proportions as there are huge quantities of gas involved.

A third example has to do with forests and oceans. Normally, they store huge amounts of CO_2 every year, but global warming has disrupted the cycle. In the future they might absorb fewer greenhouse gases and could even release some.

The precise mechanisms of these three effects are still subject to debate, as is the role global warming plays in wildfires and cloud formation. But one thing is certain: beyond a certain point, the situation spirals out of control. This is why researchers are aiming to limit the average temperature increase to 2°C in comparison with last century's average temperatures.

See also pages 89, 148 and 164.

Permafrost, Western Siberia, Russia (61°38′N, 72°50′E). Siberia covers three-quarters of Russia's surface area. It has enormous amounts of hydrocarbon and mineral deposits, but the cold climate makes the region very inhospitable. Only the extraction sites are really populated. Fifty-nine per cent of the territory is covered in permafrost (permanently frozen soil), which can reach a depth of up to 1,500 metres in Eastern Siberia.

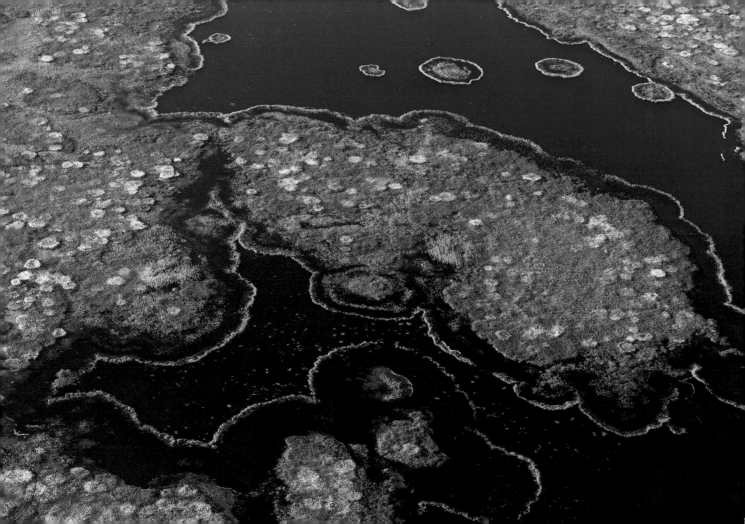

NATURAL CYCLES

What if global warming is simply the result of a natural cycle? The Earth would naturally revert to its previous state one day. Unfortunately, this is not the case. Our planet certainly experiences alternating phases of cooling and warming. These are caused by slight changes in the orbit called Milankovitch cycles. These cycles occur about every 100,000 years; the past millennia were part of a warming phase. However, the climate change that we are currently observing is taking place much faster than any previous change in the past fifty million years! Global warming is thus a separate phenomenon, which has been compounded into the original warming cycle.

Other factors, such as a change in sunlight intensity, can affect the weather. The cycles of our star last for about eleven years. But this rhythm is too short to explain the length and the extent of what we can see today. Indeed, scientists even predict that we are entering a new phase of intense solar activity that will accelerate current global warming.

The Earth has already experienced hotter periods than it is experiencing today. When studying tree rings, microscopic air bubbles trapped in ice for hundreds of thousands of years, fossilized coral deposits and the presence of certain isotopes, researchers have found a correlation with greenhouse gas concentration every time. But research has also shown that the planet has never experienced the type of change it is experiencing today. What is taking place right now is different from older cycles.

The greenhouse effect explains the phenomenon of global warming. To deny this is to avoid responsibility and to impede preventative action against human greenhouse gas emissions.

See also pages 28, 34 and 86.

> THE CLIMATE CHANGE THAT WE ARE CURRENTLY OBSERVING IS TAKING PLACE MUCH FASTER THAN ANY PREVIOUS CHANGE IN THE PAST FIFTY MILLION YEARS.

Mount Pinatubo, Luzon Island, Philippines (15°08'N, 120°21'E). In 1991 the eruption of Mount Pinatubo, one of the largest volcanic eruptions in the twentieth century, released about twenty million tons of sulphur dioxide as far up as thirty-four kilometres high. The temporary layer of aerosols created by the eruption reduced the planet's available sunlight by 2 per cent! This event led to a decrease in surface temperatures by several tenths of a degree Celsius in 1992 and 1993.

THE GULF STREAM

What if the Gulf Stream disappeared? If this warm ocean current that crosses the North Atlantic slows down, will it mean cooler temperatures in Europe?

The planet's most powerful ocean currents, like the El Niño current in the Pacific and the Gulf Stream in the Atlantic, contribute to water and heat exchanges on a global level. They are extraordinarily powerful: the Gulf Stream's rate of flow exceeds ten million cubic metres of water per second. It sometimes slows down and has even stopped before – the last time was about eight thousand years ago. Today, the Arctic's melting ice is releasing cold freshwater that is interfering with the current. The freshwater could slow it down, make it shift southwards or even stop it – but nothing is certain.

The Gulf Stream plays a role in Europe's mild winters. But to what extent? It is commonly believed that it is because of the Gulf Stream that the average winter temperature in London is 15°C higher than in Newfoundland, which is at the same latitude on the other side of the Atlantic. But it now appears the Gulf Stream only has a minor role: warm westerly winds are even more important in making the climate milder. Even if the Gulf Stream stopped, the cooling effects would not compensate for the global warming linked to the increase in the greenhouse effect. Thus, no glaciation is expected in Europe.

However, if the Gulf Stream stops, there will be other consequences: its disappearance would affect the flow of nutrients in the ocean and the life of various ecosystems. It could also have an impact on the ocean's absorption of carbon, which would in turn affect the amounts of CO_2 in the atmosphere. These are only examples, but one thing is for sure: the ocean and the atmosphere are inextricably linked, even if their relationship is still not entirely understood.

See also pages 56, 76 and 82.

> THE AVERAGE WINTER TEMPERATURE IN LONDON IS 15°C HIGHER THAN IN NEWFOUNDLAND, WHICH IS AT THE SAME LATITUDE ON THE OTHER SIDE OF THE ATLANTIC.

Upper Lough Erne, Ulster, Northern Ireland, United Kingdom (54°12'N, 7°29'W). The River Erne runs for 105 kilometres before flowing into Donegal Bay on the northwest coast of the island. After crossing the Ulster border, the river widens to form Lough Erne. The banks of this lake, popular with fishermen, are lined with hedged meshing (hedge-lined paths) that protect the coasts from erosion.

THE KILIMANJARO DEBATE

The snows of Mount Kilimanjaro are a symbol of climate change. They are also the subject of a stormy debate. Why? Because the snows that Hemingway believed to be eternal are disappearing: they have lost 80 per cent of their surface area over the past century. However, this complex phenomenon is not a good example of climate change.

The culprit is not the one many suspect: it is not an increase in global temperature that seems to be causing the phenomenon. Kilimanjaro's glacier is located at a high altitude, where the temperature rarely rises above -3°C. Additionally, the glacier started to melt long before the 1950s, when the increase in temperature first became noticeable.

The determining factor appears to be a decrease in precipitation. Glaciers advance because of snowfall and retreat because of melting or sublimation. However,

THE AIR HAS BECOME DRIER BECAUSE THERE ARE FEWER HUMID WINDS BLOWING OFF THE INDIAN OCEAN.

since the end of the nineteenth century, the climate in East Africa has changed. The air has become drier because there are fewer humid winds blowing off the Indian Ocean. This could explain why the ice is disappearing.

This does not mean that humans are without fault. Global warming is increasing this change in wind patterns and regional deforestation is making the aridity worse. Forests add humidity to the air; those below the glacier have mostly been cut down to free up land for agriculture. Since 1976, dew has decreased by about 25 per cent.

This counterexample should not overshadow the reality of climate change. Even though the ice in Kilimanjaro is not melting because of global warming, the rest of the planet's glaciers are. Over the last decade they have lost a total of three hundred billion tons of ice per year.

See also pages 28, 70 and 162.

Kilimanjaro's disappearing snows, Tanzania (3°04'S, 37°22'E). Mount Kilimanjaro, made up of three extinct volcanoes, is the highest summit in Africa (5,895 metres). Kilimanjaro's famous eternal snows, which are more than 11,000 years old, could disappear by 2020. These glaciers, estimated to have covered an area of twelve square kilometres in 1900, now only cover two square kilometres and have lost one metre of thickness.

ACCELERATION IN GREENLAND

Scientists have often been criticized for not being sure: they are frightening us with uncertain data and unverified hypotheses. But in some cases, their caution has made us underestimate the risks. This is the case in Greenland.

Until recently, specialists did not think there would be any major changes in the area. In their 2001 report, IPCC researchers noted that the overall assessment of melted ice in Greenland was not statistically significant. But in 2007, they estimated that between fifty and one hundred billion tons of ice had melted over a ten-year span from 1993 to 2003. There was even an increase in the following years. Since then, every new study has highlighted the accelerated melting, which could even reach up to two to three hundred billion tons a year.

Many factors explain this acceleration. The main one seems to be that melting ice in summer, even at normal rates, creates water currents that run deep into the ice cap until they reach the rocky substrate that makes up

ONE HUNDRED BILLION TONS OF ICE MELTED OVER A TEN-YEAR SPAN FROM 1993 TO 2003.

the biggest island in the world. The water acts as a lubricant between the ice and the rocky surface, making the ice slide towards the sea. There are other factors as well: as certain areas melt, they become thinner. This lighter, more fragile ice then slides down to the sea even faster than before. Moreover, industrial pollution generates fine dust that settles on Greenland's immaculate ice, making it less white. It is thus less reflective and absorbs more solar heat.

If Greenland's ice melts completely, the water level of the ocean will rise by almost seven metres. This means that certain countries (the Maldives and Bangladesh) and coastal cities (New York and Shanghai) could become submerged. There is still time: at the current rate, it will take about ten thousand years for all of Greenland's ice to disappear completely. But, once again, the problem is that the phenomenon is accelerating.

See also pages 14, 68 and 124.

Melt-water lake near Nordlit Sermiat, Greenland (61°05'N, 46°27'W). While sea ice floats on water, an ice sheet is located on land. In Greenland, the ice sheet, which covers an area of 1.7 million square kilometres, can be over three thousand metres thick. It alone contains almost 10 per cent of the Earth's freshwater.

DISRUPTIVE MOLECULES

The increase in the concentration of greenhouse gases in the atmosphere is unprecedented. This is shown by measurements from ice cores (different colours represent different studies) and atmospheric samples (red lines). The warming effect of these two gases is calculated using a parameter called radiative forcing.

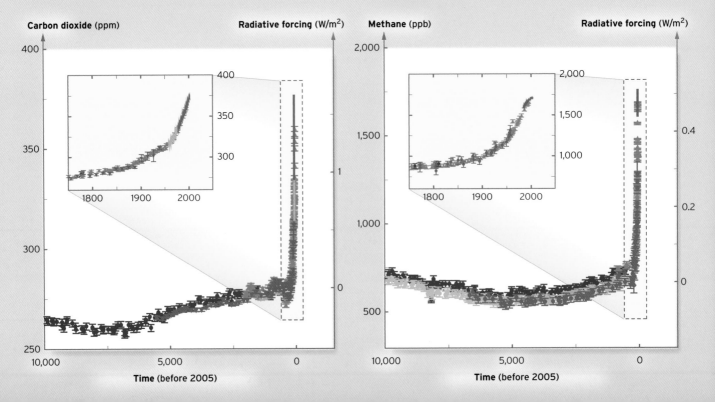

WORLD GREENHOUSE GAS EMISSIONS

Every year, humankind emits about thirty billion tons of CO_2. If the emissions of other human-related greenhouse gases are taken into account, the figure goes up to the equivalent of fifty billion tons of carbon dioxide. Emissions are continuing to increase.

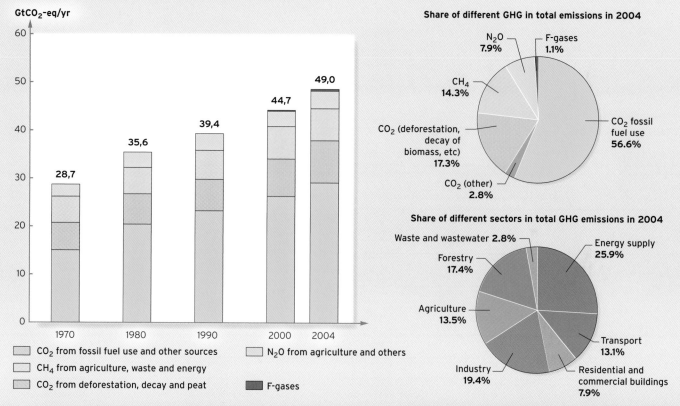

GtCO$_2$-eq/yr

28,7 (1970)
35,6 (1980)
39,4 (1990)
44,7 (2000)
49,0 (2004)

☐ CO_2 from fossil fuel use and other sources
☐ CH_4 from agriculture, waste and energy
☐ CO_2 from deforestation, decay and peat
☐ N_2O from agriculture and others
☐ F-gases

Share of different GHG in total emissions in 2004

N_2O 7.9%
F-gases 1.1%
CH_4 14.3%
CO_2 (deforestation, decay of biomass, etc) 17.3%
CO_2 (other) 2.8%
CO_2 fossil fuel use 56.6%

Share of different sectors in total GHG emissions in 2004

Waste and wastewater 2.8%
Forestry 17.4%
Agriculture 13.5%
Industry 19.4%
Energy supply 25.9%
Transport 13.1%
Residential and commercial buildings 7.9%

Patrick, *south of France*
I think that the Earth will do just fine without people. Other organisms will thrive. Nevertheless, it would be a shame if humankind were to disappear.

Patrick

Atiq

Katy

Katy, *west of Peru*
Snow will be far away, it won't exist anymore, glaciers won't exist anymore! Where will we get our water from? How will our children live, how will our grandchildren live, those people who haven't been born yet and who will wonder who is responsible.

Atiq, *Dakha, Bangladesh*

f the sea level rises one meter, about 35 million people living on the coasts
of Bangladesh will have to move. Where will they go? Logically, they should move
to where the problems were created: the rich Western countries.
say that in that near future, Bangladeshi are going to need a piece of Maryland,
a piece of Florida, a piece of Texas, and so on.

Stephen, *California, United States*
Most people, if they face a potential disaster,
will buy insurance. The probability for a house to burn down
in the West is about 1 or 2 per cent, and yet almost everyone
has home insurance. The precautionary principle
that we apply when we buy insurance
must also be applied to the planet.

SCENARIOS

Salem, *north of Mali*
This change in the climate affects even our mentality.
For us, rain is money, rain is gold. When it rains, we have everything;
when it doesn't rain, it creates unemployment and leads to crime
and many other things.

WHAT WILL BE THE WEATHER TOMORROW?

Nobody can tell what the weather will be like in a few days, so how can we predict what the weather will be like in ten years or one hundred? Will it be hot? Very hot? Probably. But scientists don't want to be perceived as astrologers or fortune tellers.

The IPCC bases its scenarios on mathematical models that use the planet's most powerful computers. The atmosphere and ocean are divided into hundreds of millions of cubes. Their evolution is then calculated gradually. On a yearly scale, local meteorological variations seem insignificant.

The models are verified in several ways. They are examined in reverse to see if they can trace past changes accurately. Then they are tested to see if they can take the most recent data into account. They are also compared to one other; there are many models (e.g. GISS-ER, HadCM3), each attached to a different research centre. But none of the results are perfect: for example, researchers freely admit that they have difficulty imitating the role of clouds – this is obviously an essential parameter. This is why they provide ranges of values: for example, by 2099 the precipitation decrease in southern Europe could be from -4 per cent to -27 per cent.

But most importantly, these models establish scenarios for the next century, not predictions. They are possible stories or 'narrative frameworks', not future reality. Researchers know that the future will be different from these scenarios. But by providing several benchmarks, they show how our planet could evolve in one direction or another. They give us the tools we need to reflect and make decisions.

See also pages 64, 88 and 186.

> THESE MODELS ESTABLISH SCENARIOS FOR THE NEXT CENTURY, NOT PREDICTIONS. THEY ARE POSSIBLE STORIES, NOT FUTURE REALITY.

Louis S. St-Laurent icebreaker, Resolute Bay, Nunavut territory, Canada (74°42'N, 95°18'W). Arctic sea ice and glacier ice are casualties of global warming. In 2008, for the first time since data has been available, the Northwest Passage and the Northeast Passage (through the Arctic Ocean) were both ice-free at the same time. If the ice keeps melting at the current rate, summer pack ice in the Arctic could disappear before 2020.

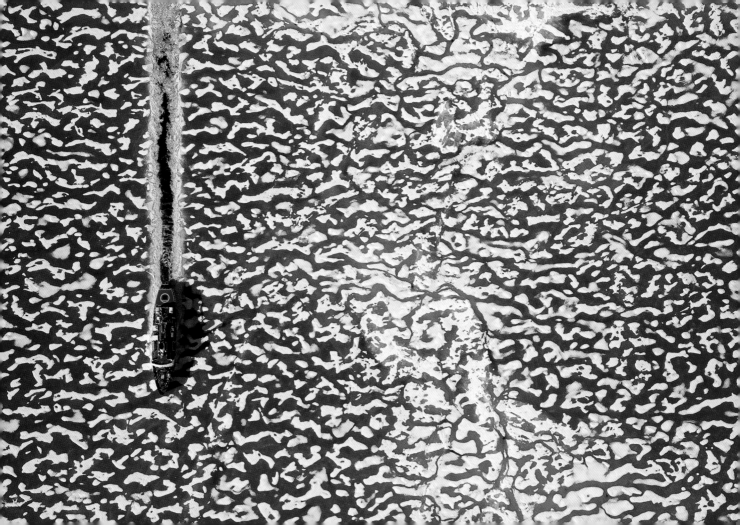

6.4 DEGREES WARMER

What will the world look like if we keep up with business as usual and don't change our habits? The Gross World Product (GWP) could increase ten to twenty-six-fold by 2100 when compared to 1990. Our greenhouse gas emissions will increase in the same way. But how exactly?

Thirty future scenarios have been proposed, which are grouped into four main categories: A1, A2, B1 and B2. The first two categories are based on rapid economic growth, with a more globalized world in A1 than in A2. The other two categories are based on slower, more environmentally conscious growth with a more globalized world in B1 than in B2. Researchers use these hypotheses to calculate greenhouse gas emissions and then calculate the concentration of gas in the atmosphere. They can estimate factors such as average temperature, rising sea levels and changes in precipitation.

THE GROSS WORLD PRODUCT COULD INCREASE TEN TO TWENTY-SIX-FOLD BY 2100 WHEN COMPARED TO 1990. OUR GREENHOUSE GAS EMISSIONS WILL INCREASE IN THE SAME WAY.

In these scenarios, the type of energy used is important. If cleaner technology makes it possible to use less energy or to emit less greenhouse gases, this will affect the scenarios. For example, the A1 group has three possible options: A1FI (mostly fossil fuels), A1T (mostly non-fossil fuels) and A1B (balance). The average global warming at the end of this century ranges from 1.4°C to 3.8°C for A1T and from 2.4°C to 6.4°C for A1FI – almost twice as much with the fossil-fuel scenario.

The economy is not the only factor: demographic, social and political variables also play a role and have been taken into account. For instance, if there are fifteen billion human beings in 2100 rather than seven billion, greenhouse gas emissions will increase significantly. These scenarios reflect the choices that societies may make.

See also pages 86, 92 and 186.

Women grinding millet near Bandiagara, Mopti region, Mali (14°20'N, 3°37'W). The Dogons, who number about three hundred thousand, have lived as farmers in central Mali for five centuries. In this country fighting for food self-sufficiency, 80 per cent of the population makes a living from agriculture, which is now threatened by encroaching deserts.

VIRTUAL

Scenarios

Will a virtual economy emit less CO_2? When a scenario with a service-and-information economy (type B1) is compared with a more standard evolution (type A1), emissions are almost halved.

According to a European study, the dematerialization of the economy – replacing products or carbon-rich activities with their virtual or electronic equivalents – could reduce energy consumption in buildings by 17 per cent and transport emissions by 27 per cent (by improving logistics operations).

We should not overestimate the importance of this technology. Substituting 20 per cent of business trips with videoconferences would reduce CO_2 emissions by about twenty-five million tons a year – although this is not much compared to the thirty billion tons emitted every year. And even if you do your shopping on the internet, it still has to be delivered to your home, which requires a motor vehicle.

AN INTERNET SERVER EMITS AS MUCH GREENHOUSE GAS OVER A YEAR AS AN SUV.

Additionally, information and communication technologies (ICT) emit significant amounts of greenhouse gases: about 2 per cent of world emissions (1.75 per cent through use and 0.25 per cent to produce equipment). This is as much as the aeronautical industry! An internet server emits as much greenhouse gas over a year as an SUV because it is almost always working, usually in an air-conditioned data centre. Even a single search on Google or a virtual character in a game or parallel universe consumes energy.

But if the results of the B1 scenario are much better, it is not only because of the digital economy, but also because it includes 'a high level of social and environmental responsibility combined with a global approach to sustainable development'. Virtual reality is, apparently, only part of the solution.

See also pages 106, 116 and 158.

Parabolic antennas on rooftops in Aleppo, Syria (36°13'N, 37°10'E). Aleppo, one of the oldest towns in the world, has not escaped modernisation. A forest of parabolic antennas picks up television programmes from all over the world, relayed from space by satellites. Television is now one of the most popular forms of media in the world. Literacy is not required to watch television, which makes it more accessible.

ENVIRONMENTAL REFUGEES

The first atolls flooded as a result of global warming were Tebua, Tarawa and Abanuea in the Republic of Kiribati. Located in the Pacific Ocean, they disappeared beneath the water in 1999 – luckily, they were uninhabited. However, since sea levels are predicted to rise, most island nations will be threatened: Tuvalu (with a high point of four metres above sea level) has experienced its first waves of emigration. Papua New Guinea was the first to organize part of its population's collective displacement: 2,600 inhabitants from the Carteret Islands.

But they are not the only places that are threatened. Many of the world's largest cities, like New York, Shanghai and London, are near the sea. The river deltas of the Nile, the Mekong and the Ganges – which millions of people depend upon – are especially vulnerable. In fact, a large part of the world's population lives by the sea. Most of them will have to move: they will become environmental migrants or 'eco-refugees'.

CLIMATE REFUGEES ARE NOT RECOGNIZED BY ANY INTERNATIONAL LAWS, LIKE THE GENEVA CONVENTIONS.

Global warming will cause harsher droughts, increasingly frequent flooding and more dangerous storms. Even people who live far from the coast may have to leave their homes. Global warming could result in a total of 250 million refugees.

Today, these refugees are not recognized by any international laws, like the Geneva Conventions. This makes it difficult to protect and care for them. Tuvalu is a prime example: to prepare for the exodus, the government requested emigration visas for their citizens from neighbouring countries. New Zealand accepted with certain conditions, but Australia did not. This is particularly unfair: island nations emit very few greenhouse gases in comparison with large countries like Australia, which is a major emitter.

The issue of status for environmental refugees is linked to responsibility. The subject is being debated by specialists in international law, for the moment to no avail. *See also pages 16, 84 and 124.*

Flooded house south of Dhaka, Bangladesh (23°21'N, 90°31'E). In 1998, two-thirds of Bangladesh was under water for several months. This was the result of the strongest flood of the twentieth century, which killed 1,300 people and destroyed the homes of thirty-one million Bangladeshi. About twenty million Bangladeshi may need to move before 2020 in order to flee the gradual submersion of their land.

FRESHWATER

There is a consequence of global warming that is perhaps even more of a cause for concern than rising sea levels: the water shortage that will be caused by melting glaciers. Today, glacial ice supplies water to most of the planet's major rivers. The glaciers of the Himalayas and the Tibetan plateau are the source of Asia's mightiest rivers – the Yellow, the Yangtze, the Mekong, the Ganges and the Indus – which together irrigate an area inhabited by two billion people!

At first, the melting ice will cause an overabundance of water. In the mountainous regions, this will cause sudden, disastrous flooding. Lower down, the monsoon will cause gentler but more severe overflow. Flooding may peak around 2050, destroying crops and homes near rivers. Asia is not the only continent under threat: Europe has also experienced disastrous floods – in France in 1999 and in Central Europe in 2002 and 2005. In South America, the Andes region is following a similar pattern.

THE GLACIERS OF THE HIMALAYAS AND THE TIBETAN PLATEAU TOGETHER IRRIGATE AN AREA INHABITED BY TWO BILLION PEOPLE.

The water shortage will then begin, because global warming will shorten winters and reduce the amount of snowfall. The ice that melts in summer will no longer be renewed. After a few decades, there will no longer be enough ice to supply rivers. Certain Indian rivers could become seasonal in the second half of the twentieth century. And yet, the current rate of flow of the Brahmaputra, to name but one, is one hundred times stronger than the rate of flow of European rivers such as the Seine, the Ebro or the Tiber!

In addition to drinking water and irrigation resources, energy production is also under threat. This is because hydroelectric dams won't be able to provide as much energy and thermal power stations will experience cooling problems. People will have to adapt to a new world, leave more dangerous areas, change farming practices and set up new water management systems.

See also pages 76, 80 and 108.

Mount Himalchuli, Himalayas, Nepal (28°26'N, 84°39'E). Mount Himalchuli is 7,893 metres high. The increase in regional temperatures (+1°C since 1970) has caused Himalayan glaciers to begin melting. They could disappear in as little as forty years, depriving populations downstream of an indispensable resource for irrigation.

TOWARDS FOOD SHORTAGES?

Will global warming make the world's food insecurity worse? Agriculture is highly dependant on the climate, and farming practices are going to change in the coming years. However, it is hard to get an overall picture because scenarios are so varied.

A slight temperature increase (between 1 and 2°C) will improve productivity at high and middle latitudes. In Europe, yields could increase by 30 per cent. The northern boundary of agriculture will move a few hundred kilometres northwards. However, increased flooding and droughts will threaten crops and maybe even create food shortages.

A higher temperature increase (between 2 and 3°C) will mean that the negative effects will have greater impact. The loss of arable land through desertification will worsen and neutralise the positive effects elsewhere on the planet.

With a temperature increase of more than 3°C, major secondary effects will become apparent. The amount of water needed for irrigation will increase by 5 to 20 per cent depending on the region. Developing countries – often located at lower latitudes, especially in Africa – will have to import more food. The price of agricultural products will increase proportionally. In total, an additional 40 to 170 million people will suffer from hunger, mainly in Africa. In parallel, the increase in CO_2 concentration, which will certainly exceed 500 ppm, will have a positive effect: it will activate photosynthesis and therefore increase agricultural production. But the overall result will be negative.

As always, the weakest populations will be hit the hardest. But, in any case, the extent of the changes will depend on our reaction. Agricultural politics, farming practices and socioeconomic development will have more effect than global warming itself.

See also pages 24, 46 and 108.

> AGRICULTURE IS HIGHLY DEPENDANT ON THE CLIMATE, AND FARMING PRACTICES ARE GOING TO CHANGE IN THE COMING YEARS.

Potato harvest near Arba, Algeria (36°34'N, 3°08'E). The Mitidja Plain extends in an arc for over one hundred kilometres from the edge of Algiers. Generations of Algerians have reclaimed this land, which used to be marshes, transforming it into one of the country's most beautiful agricultural plains. Fertile soil and adequate rainfall make it possible to grow crops such as potatoes, rice and grapes.

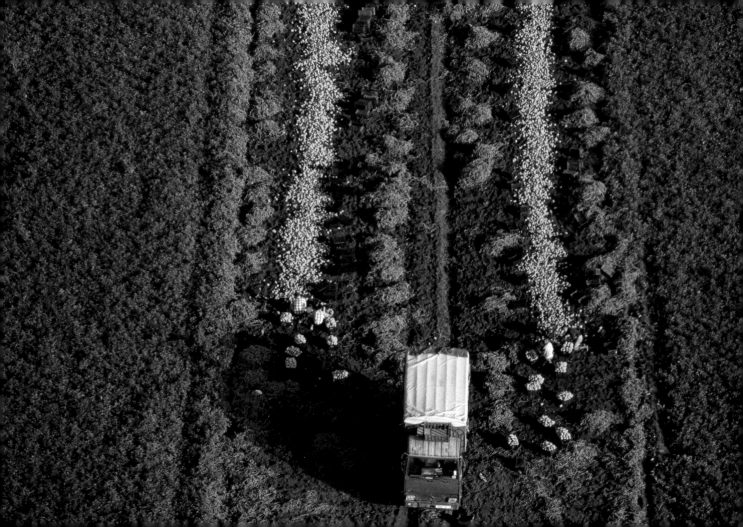

EXTINCTIONS

Polar bears will not be the only species to disappear because of global warming. Many other species – less visible or symbolic – will also be endangered. For these species, global warming is the last straw; humans have already subjected the environment to great pressure: the destruction of habitats, environmental fragmentation and pollution, to name a few. If the temperature increases by 2 to 3°C, about one-third of all species will face an increased risk of extinction.

It all depends on the pace. The living world is constantly evolving and has adapted to many environmental changes. But global warming causes rapid changes in ecosystems. These will probably happen too fast for many living organisms to adapt in time.

Arctic regions and coral reefs are the most vulnerable ecosystems. An increase of just 1°C can destroy the symbiosis between coral and the microscopic algae it needs to survive; the loss of this algae makes coral whiten

ARCTIC REGIONS AND CORAL REEFS ARE THE MOST VULNERABLE ECOSYSTEMS.

and die. Savannahs and deserts have the least vulnerable ecosystems. Even 'virgin' areas where humans are not (very) present – like the heart of the Amazon forest or tundra regions – could be affected, because the climate's evolution affects the entire planet.

Today, the Earth is facing its sixth mass extinction. After each previous extinction, biodiversity has undergone new phases of diversification and expansion. But today, only one species – *Homo sapiens* – bears responsibility. And we could also become a victim. Even if the extinction of the polar bear seems no more than a symbol, the disappearance of coral would be disastrous: coral reefs host one-fourth of all marine species! Insects pollinate plants and recycle our waste. Mangrove swamps act as buffers against storms, floods and soil erosion. These are but a few examples.

See also pages 22 and 118.

Elephants in the Okavango Delta, Botswana (19°26'S, 23°03'E). African elephants travel great distances to find the one to two hundred kilograms of vegetation they need for their daily diet. Hunted for their ivory, they nearly went extinct in the twentieth century. Their population dropped from 2.5 million in 1945 to five hundred thousand in 1989, when the ivory trade was banned. Today, there are only about three hundred thousand elephants remaining, mostly on confined reserves.

PRECIPITATION

A hotter world will also be more humid. Heat increases evaporation, especially above the oceans, which cover two-thirds of the globe's surface. Heat also increases the amount of water vapour that air can retain. And the water that goes up must come down.

This increase in precipitation will not be insignificant: it could rise by 20 per cent over the next century. However, as is often the case with climate phenomena, the global effect overshadows the wide range of situations on a local level. Precipitation will increase in tropical areas and at high altitudes, but it will decrease in subtropical areas. Put simply, in areas where it is already raining, it will rain more; in semi-arid areas, it will rain even less. In Europe, the summers will be drier and the winters will be more wet.

Rain will also be more intense on average: the rain that falls will be torrential rather than just showers. But ecosystems, especially vegetation, can only absorb a limited amount of water. Beyond this point, it drains away and can cause flooding, mudslides, and so on. It also causes erosion. Rather than allowing vegetation to grow better, this extra water will have a negative effect on ecosystems.

A temperature increase also means an increase in the energy in the atmosphere. This will be released during extreme phenomena such as cyclones, whose intensity is linked – among other things – to the temperature of the sea water above which they form. They will become more powerful and will affect more areas in the world. Some precipitation, like the extra snow that will fall on glaciers, will have a positive effect. Unfortunately, it will not be enough to counterbalance the increasing melting or stop their disappearance.

See also pages 20, 70 and 80.

THE INCREASE IN PRECIPITATION COULD RISE BY 20 PER CENT OVER THE NEXT CENTURY.

Storm over the Amazon forest near Tefé, Brazil (3°32'S, 64°53'W). With an area of 3.7 million square kilometres, the Amazon is the largest tropical forest ecosystem in the world and makes up one-third of the planet's tropical forests. It is home to half of the world's biodiversity. Each day, nearly two hundred square kilometres of forest disappear along with a considerable number of species, whose secrets we will never know.

HEALTH

According to an estimate by the World Health Organization, climate change could already be causing one hundred and fifty thousand deaths a year. This number could double by 2030. The phenomenon is threatening all the principal factors that affect health: a mild climate, clean water, adequate food and shelter.

Malaria and dengue fever are two devastating diseases linked to the climate through mosquitoes. Because of the effects of global warming, mosquitoes will migrate to regions that have become hotter and more humid, and the risk of infection may increase in southern European countries. But Africa – where malaria already kills one million people every year – will be the worst hit. The disease will threaten an additional one-third of the continent's population before the end of the century.

Malnutrition will worsen. Because of the higher CO_2 levels in the atmosphere, plants like cassava root, a staple food for an estimated one billion people by 2030, will be less productive and less rich in protein. More frequent droughts and floods will also reduce agricultural yields. Moreover, they will make it harder to access clean water.

As a result, the number of cases of cholera and other intestinal diseases will increase from 2 to 5 per cent by 2020 in low-income countries. Cholera already kills two million children every year.

The difference in sanitary conditions between rich and poor countries will increase. In cities, heat and stagnant air will leave more pollutants in the air and cause more cardiorespiratory diseases. However, high-income countries in Europe, the United States and East Asia will be protected by their public health systems. Poorer populations will feel the full brunt of global warming, even though they contributed little to it.

See also pages 72, 86 and 120.

> THE NUMBER OF CASES OF CHOLERA AND OTHER INTESTINAL DISEASES WILL INCREASE FROM 2 TO 5 PER CENT BY 2020 IN LOW-INCOME COUNTRIES.

Raised huts in Makoko shanty town, Lagos Lagoon, Nigeria (6°30'N, 3°24'E). There are now probably more than ten million people living in Lagos, the former capital of Africa's most populous country. Makoko, its lagoon shanty town, has no running water, electricity or public sewage system. Its inhabitants live in huts built on stilts that can only be accessed by canoe.

DESERTIFICATION

It may seem like a paradox to talk about desertification in a world where precipitation is going to increase, but it is a real possibility. The scenarios are relatively vague about what will happen to semi-arid regions like the Sahel, Australia, the Mediterranean Basin, the southwestern United States, southern Africa and the Brazilian *sertão*. However, those living in these fragile regions are at the mercy of environmental changes.

Desertification, defined as the degradation of soil and a reduction in its organic productivity, can even occur in regions that get enough rainfall. Collecting wood for cooking reduces the number of trees. Overgrazing, soil impoverishment, erosion and the over-exploitation of non-renewable groundwater also degrade humankind's living conditions.

What will global warming do to the Sahel, an eight-hundred-kilometre-wide strip of land that stretches for seven thousand kilometres, from Senegal to Sudan? The

THE AFRICAN MONSOON BRINGS THE YEAR'S ONLY MAJOR RAINFALL. IT IS THREATENED BY CLIMATE CHANGE.

Sahel links tropical Africa to the south with the Sahara – the world's largest desert – to the north. If the African monsoon does not come, famine will strike farmers and herders as it brings the year's only major rainfall, from July to September. The recurrent droughts in the 1970s and 1980s are an example of what might happen. Climatologists believe developing global warming could already have been part of the problem.

Climatologists are cautious when speaking about the twenty-first century, but models indicate an increased variability in the African monsoon. Some models show an increase in precipitation in the Sahel by 20 to 30 per cent towards the middle of the century. However, the temperature increase will heighten evaporation. This will have a major impact as animal husbandry and farming are key resources for African populations.

See also pages 20, 24 and 72.

Village near Tom Marefin, Chad (12°30'N, 14°55'E). One of these very green trees, probably the one in the middle, is a palaver tree, where people gather in the shade. The villagers and their livestock use the paths every day, especially to go to the well or collect wood. Rainfall here is too low for rain-fed agriculture.

WINNERS AND LOSERS

Some people will give up on global warming, particularly if the effects remain moderate. In fact, the climate in certain inhospitable regions will become milder and unproductive land will become farmable. Soil productivity could increase in Canada, Russia and southern Argentina.

The Arctic region is symbolic of future opportunities, especially with the end of the year-round ice pack: with no more sea ice, the region will become navigable. The dream of the great nineteenth-century explorers, to go from the Atlantic to the Pacific via the Arctic, will finally come true as the Northwest Passage will open up.

By going north of Canada, freighters travelling between Europe and Asia will no longer need to pass through the Panama Canal. The Tokyo-Rotterdam route – currently twenty-three thousand kilometres long – will be shortened to sixteen thousand kilometres. By going north of Russia through the Northeast Passage, the route will only be fourteen thousand kilometres long.

The Arctic substratum may also contain huge undiscovered deposits of gas, oil, diamonds and gold. These deposits, previously protected by an extreme climate and a layer of ice, will now be easier to exploit.

For these reasons, the Arctic will become a zone of economic interest and geopolitical strategy. Canada, Russia, Denmark, the United States and Norway are already undertaking intense diplomatic efforts to reinforce their control in the region. Until now, the borders in this part of the world have not always been established accurately.

But for the original inhabitants of the Arctic – the Inuit, the Sami and the Nenets – new influxes of money and development mean new challenges. Their way of life and their culture could be threatened by environmental changes as well as political and economic developments. *See also pages 86, 150 and 186.*

> THE DREAM OF THE GREAT NINETEENTH-CENTURY EXPLORERS, TO GO FROM THE ATLANTIC TO THE PACIFIC VIA THE ARCTIC, WILL FINALLY COME TRUE.

Autumn forest in the Charlevoix region, Canada (47°40'N, 71°02'W). The hills in Charlevoix, Quebec, which borders the Saint Lawrence River, are covered by a mixed forest of deciduous trees and conifers. The forest, covering over half of Quebec, has been exploited since the end of the seventeenth century. In June 2008 about 138 million hectares of Canadian forest were certified as sustainable.

A NEW WORLD ORDER

Since 2003, the Pentagon has shown an official interest in climate change. While the Bush administration may have officially denied the existence of global warming, American generals had already published a report on the subject and given the matter strategic consideration. They are not the only ones: armies around the world are preparing for possible climate change scenarios, despite the uncertainties.

Melting ice will change some borders. Switzerland and Italy have had to redefine their common border, which follows an icy ridge. These negotiations focused on inhabited zones and took place peacefully, but territorial matters can be delicate. Melting glaciers could fuel tensions in Kashmir, a territory disputed by India and Pakistan, where three wars have already been fought. In the Arctic, melting ice will change the area's geography. Territorial claims in this resource-rich region are a controversial issue for the neigbouring nations. Two of these, the United States and Russia, are powerful rivals with nuclear weapons.

> MELTING GLACIERS COULD FUEL TENSIONS IN KASHMIR, A TERRITORY DISPUTED BY INDIA AND PAKISTAN, WHERE THREE WARS HAVE ALREADY BEEN FOUGHT.

The possibility of millions of environmental refugees throughout the world is causing concern. As can be seen in recent events in Darfur and the Democratic Republic of the Congo, population displacement can destabilize a region and inflame conflicts. As a preventive measure, India has reinforced its border with Bangladesh, which is threatened by rising sea levels. Future climate disasters mean armed forces will have to be involved in new types of policing and humanitarian missions – like after Hurricane Katrina, for example.

Climate issues may lead to global security problems; preventing global warming means striving for peace. This is one of the reasons why the IPCC and Al Gore were awarded the Nobel Peace Prize for their work on the subject.

See also pages 68, 162 and 186.

Rock of Gibraltar, British territory, Gibraltar (36°07'N, 5°21'W). Though Spain has often laid claim to Gibraltar, it has been a British colony since an Anglo-Dutch fleet captured it in 1704. The Strait of Gibraltar separates the Moroccan and Spanish coasts by fifteen kilometres; illegal immigrants use it as a passage into Europe.

CLIMATE JUSTICE

The Competitive Enterprise Institute (CEI), America's largest 'sceptical' lobby group, once created an advert in favour of CO_2 with the slogan, 'Carbon is life'. They argue that CO_2 is the root of photosynthesis and, therefore, life. They also argue that CO_2 production is the result of economic development that has significantly improved the general population's daily living standards – in the United States, at least. They have made a plea in favour of the molecule most responsible for global warming.

Sceptics argue that global warming is not as serious as believed. According to them, specialists' estimates are consistently focused on the most disastrous aspects. Sceptics believe that the suggested solution – limiting CO_2 emissions – is costing society much more (in terms of production and unemployment, for example) than the problem it is supposed to be solving. This was before the economic crisis. Once again, it is hard to know what tomorrow holds, but this argument goes against all available scientific research.

THERE IS NO RISK OF TOTAL EXTINCTION, AS WITH THE DINOSAURS.

Of course, the other extreme is also incorrect: the idea that the entirety of human existence could be threatened by global warming. Indeed, the worst-case scenarios imagine devastating social and sanitary catastrophes. The total number of people on Earth might decrease significantly. But there is no risk of total extinction, as with the dinosaurs. Even if only a few hundred thousand human beings survive, the world's population will be the size it was one hundred thousand years ago.

As with all environmental issues, the most fragile populations – the poorest people – will suffer the most. Climate change is above all a social issue: how to best spread out the effects of future changes so that they will be easier to bear for the greatest number of people. *See also pages 28, 86 and 150.*

Dugout canoe on the Niger River, near Timbuktu, Mali (16°38'N, 3°00'W). The Niger, the third-longest river in Africa (4,200 kilometres), has its headwaters in the Fouta Djalon highland region in Guinea. It runs through nine countries and supports over 110 million people along its banks. But a decrease in rainfall since 1970 has reduced the river's flow rate; it is now silting up.

SIX SCENARIOS FOR THE TWENTY–FIRST CENTURY

The IPCC has established several scenarios that explore the possible futures of a world without climate policies. Type A scenarios are based on rapid economic growth, with a more globalized world in A1 than in A2. Within this group are three possible energy options: A1FI (mostly fossil fuels), A1T (mostly non-fossil fuels) and A1B (balance). Type B scenarios are based on slower, more environmentally conscious growth. Here again, the options are more globalized in B1 than in B2. The margin of error is shown on the right.

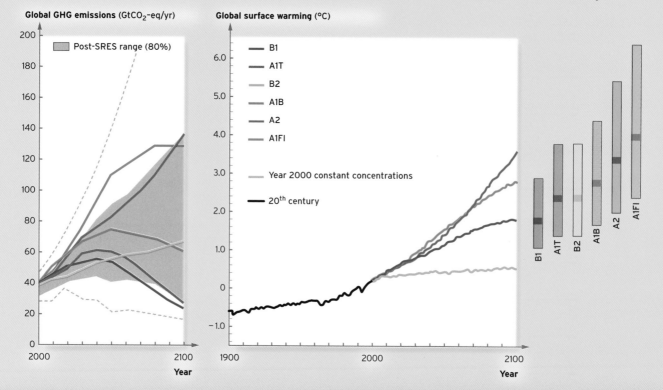

Global GHG emissions (GtCO$_2$-eq/yr)

Post-SRES range (80%)

Global surface warming (°C)

- B1
- A1T
- B2
- A1B
- A2
- A1FI

- Year 2000 constant concentrations
- 20th century

B1 A1T B2 A1B A2 A1FI

CONSEQUENCES OF GLOBAL WARMING

As the temperature rises, more and more serious pheno-mena appear in the scenarios. The most dramatic occur after the average temperature has increased more than 2°C from twentieth-century levels. This is why scientists have set 2°C as the limit that should not be exceeded.

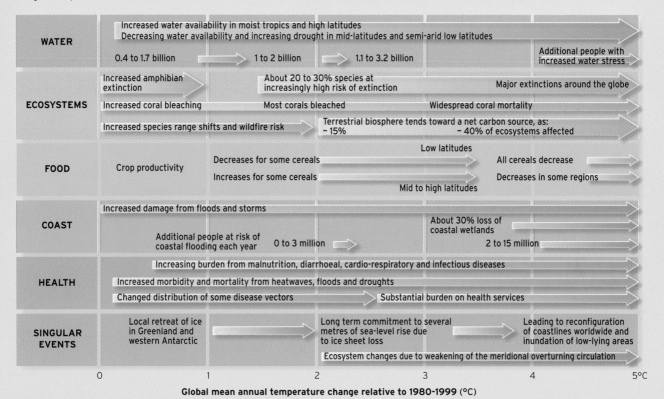

WATER	Increased water availability in moist tropics and high latitudes Decreasing water availability and increasing drought in mid-latitudes and semi-arid low latitudes				
	0.4 to 1.7 billion	1 to 2 billion	1.1 to 3.2 billion		Additional people with increased water stress
ECOSYSTEMS	Increased amphibian extinction	About 20 to 30% species at increasingly high risk of extinction		Major extinctions around the globe	
	Increased coral bleaching	Most corals bleached		Widespread coral mortality	
	Increased species range shifts and wildfire risk	Terrestrial biosphere tends toward a net carbon source, as: ~ 15% ~ 40% of ecosystems affected			
FOOD	Crop productivity	Decreases for some cereals	Low latitudes	All cereals decrease	
		Increases for some cereals	Mid to high latitudes	Decreases in some regions	
COAST	Increased damage from floods and storms				
	Additional people at risk of coastal flooding each year	0 to 3 million		About 30% loss of coastal wetlands 2 to 15 million	
HEALTH	Increasing burden from malnutrition, diarrhoeal, cardio-respiratory and infectious diseases				
	Increased morbidity and mortality from heatwaves, floods and droughts				
	Changed distribution of some disease vectors		Substantial burden on health services		
SINGULAR EVENTS	Local retreat of ice in Greenland and western Antarctic	Long term commitment to several metres of sea-level rise due to ice sheet loss		Leading to reconfiguration of coastlines worldwide and inundation of low-lying areas	
	Ecosystem changes due to weakening of the meridional overturning circulation				

0   1   2   3   4   5°C

Global mean annual temperature change relative to 1980-1999 (°C)

Abdoulaye, *north of Mali*
Instead of going to the moon,
instead of making bombs, people
should think about developing
countries where women,
children and men die.

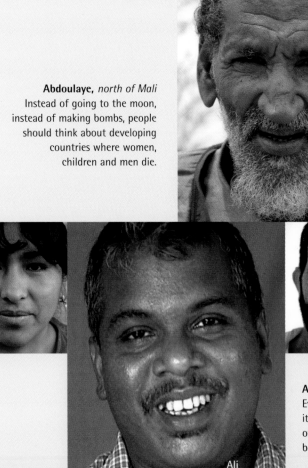

Abdoulaye

Jean

Ali

Ali, *Maldive Islands*
Even if the industrialised countries change to renewable energy,
it will be too late for us in island countries. That's why we should think
of a backup plan. We have to adapt by ourselves. We should also migrate,
because we are afraid of drowning here.

90

Jean, *south of France*

I am convinced that humankind has the ability to find the right answers; but above all, we must dispense with the myth that technology solves everything. It can help, but the solution lies mainly in our daily actions.

Hedda, *California, United States*
The first thing we should do is to educate people. I work with a lot of children, and they understand, they get it. They've been learning about this since they were young, from their teachers or from other people that might influence them. I think that many adults don't understand as well as children do.

Hedda

SOLUTIONS

Martin, *Hamburg, Germany*
Humans will always find solutions for themselves: people will build houses on stilts to avoid rising water levels, we will build storm-resistant houses, we will find technical solutions. But what will happen to the birds that I love so much, the ones flying over my town of Hamburg? What will happen to the trees and the plants that grow here?

Martin

STABILIZING THE CLIMATE

Solutions

There is no miracle solution to climate change. Today, no one technology or method will solve the problem. Each has disadvantages that will become greater on a large scale. Methods that work in one particular country or region will not necessarily work in another.

Nevertheless, there is a whole range of options we can use to stabilize the cause of the problem: greenhouse gas emissions. These options deal with energy efficiency, energy substitution, capturing and storing carbon, nuclear energy and how society is organized. Each possibility must be evaluated in relation to the others.

For instance, installing two million one-megawatt wind turbines would reduce CO_2 emissions by about one billion tons a year. This is the equivalent of removing half of the world's cars. But choosing a solution is not easy. It is an economic matter (How much does it cost? Does it take away from other investments, like health or education?), a social matter (Who wants wind turbines and who does not?) and an environmental matter (What are the secondary effects on a large scale?).

Even if we start using the available solutions immediately, it is no longer possible to avoid extensive global warming. We must be prepared for a different world. Researchers call this adaptation. For a long time, this was a contentious subject because adapting could be considered a form of defeatism and an excuse to stop fighting global warming. This is no longer the case; global warming is such an important issue that there is no longer any choice. Both strategies are necessary. The sooner action is taken, the easier it will be to implement strategies and the less it will cost.

See also pages 114, 148 and 186.

> THERE IS NO MIRACLE SOLUTION TO CLIMATE CHANGE. TODAY, NO ONE TECHNOLOGY OR METHOD WILL SOLVE THE PROBLEM.

Energy production plant in Hvidovre on the Baltic Sea, Denmark (55°39′N, 12°29′E). Located southeast of Copenhagen on the shores of the Baltic Sea, this thermal power station works using the cogeneration process. It produces heat and electricity at the same time. It also uses many types of fuel (renewable and fossil fuels) together with new procedures that reduce toxic emissions by up to 80 per cent.

SOLAR ENERGY

The Earth receives more energy from the sun in one hour than humankind consumes over the course of an entire year. If we learned how to efficiently exploit this resource, the energy problems we are currently facing would be solved.

Different techniques have already been developed. One method is to heat liquid that flows through dark piping beneath glass panes facing the sun. Today, two hundred million Chinese people have solar water heaters. It is also possible to generate electricity with photovoltaic cells. Even though it is not yet used on a large scale, solar power is the world's fastest-growing source of energy. Since 2000, there has been a nine-fold increase in production.

In concentrating solar thermal power plants, mirrors concentrate the sun's rays, which are used to heat a fluid. This in turn powers a turbine that produces electricity. Theoretically, with this technology, sixty thousand square kilometres of desert with strong sunshine would be enough to generate enough energy for the entire world.

EVEN THOUGH IT IS NOT YET USED ON A LARGE SCALE, SOLAR POWER IS THE WORLD'S FASTEST-GROWING SOURCE OF ENERGY. SINCE 2000, THERE HAS BEEN A NINE-FOLD INCREASE IN PRODUCTION.

However, making power stations work is difficult; photoelectric cells are not very efficient and building them causes pollution and requires a lot of energy. Currently, solar energy only accounts for 0.039 per cent of world electricity consumption, but this technology is developing rapidly. Some experts believe it will account for 25 per cent of world consumption by 2040.

Either way, photoelectric cells have a real advantage: electricity can be produced locally, even for those who are not connected to the grid. Today, 1.7 billion people live without electricity. Even in developed countries, local - or decentralized - energy production can be advantageous. Different resources (solar, wind and others) can be combined, reducing the energy loss and pollution caused by the current system.

See also pages 98, 114 and 176.

Sanlúcar la Mayor thermoelectric solar power stations, Spain (37°26'N, 6°15'W). The large plains around Seville are sunny for 320 days a year and are therefore ideal for solar thermoelectric power stations. The first power station at this complex - there will be eight in total - is made up of 624,121 square metres of swivelling mirrors. By 2013, the eight power stations will provide electricity for 180,000 homes, the equivalent of a town like Seville.

WIND ENERGY

Wind turbines, which use a clean, renewable energy source, seem like the perfect example of eco-friendly energy. Major technological advances over the past few years has increased their size; some are over one hundred metres in diameter and their power has increased proportionally. A large wind turbine now generates more than one megawatt (MW) of electricity, which is equal to the amount consumed by one thousand Europeans (excluding heating). This reduces CO_2 emissions by about one thousand tons a year. The most powerful wind turbines are installed out at sea, where winds are more regular and they do not bother those who feel they mar the landscape. These wind turbines can generate up to five MW of power.

Wind turbines already provide almost 20 per cent of electricity in Denmark, 10 per cent in Spain and Portugal, and 7 per cent in Germany and Ireland. However, on a world scale, wind energy is not yet widespread and only accounts for 1.5 per cent of electricity.

A LARGE WIND TURBINE NOW GENERATES MORE THAN ONE MEGAWATT (MW) OF ELECTRICITY, WHICH IS EQUAL TO THE AMOUNT CONSUMED BY ONE THOUSAND PEOPLE THIS REDUCES CO_2 EMISSIONS BY ABOUT ONE THOUSAND TONS A YEAR.

How much can it increase by? Probably not much more than it already has in Denmark, because wind energy cannot substitute for other sources of energy: it is additional energy that depends on the weather. Wind turbines do not operate continuously, nor do they function when consumption peaks. They need to be used in combination with other easily adaptable forms of energy.

This is something all renewable forms of energy have in common: none of them can replace oil by themselves. But together, if they are combined with energy saving measures, they can provide an 'energy mix' that can help people develop an economy that pollutes less. The wind sector also provides jobs: it now employs 150,000 people. By 2020, this figure could be more than 300,000. This is an example of how environmentalism creates 'green jobs' that help to develop the economy and the technology, research and employment sectors.

See also pages 98, 116 and 172.

Middelgrunden offshore wind farm, off the coast of Copenhagen, Denmark (55°41'N, 12°40'E). Since the end of 2000, there has been wind farm in the Øresund Straits, which separate Denmark from Sweden. Located two kilometres east of Copenhagen's port, it is one of Denmark's largest offshore wind farms. Its twenty aerogenerators each have a seventy-six-metre diameter rotor and are perched sixty-four metres above the water. This farm produces eighty-nine million kW a year, or about 3 per cent of the city's electricity.

SAVING ENERGY

The cheapest, least pollutive energy is energy that is not consumed. We can save energy in all areas of everyday life: transportation, housing, domestic appliances... Saving energy on a daily basis is the most effective means of reducing greenhouse gas emissions. It could reduce greenhouse gas emissions by sixty billion tons of CO_2 by 2030.

If all European Union citizens replaced their incandescent light bulbs with energy-saving bulbs – a step that is gradually becoming compulsory – they would save the equivalent of the annual production of ten electric power stations and would reduce CO_2 emissions by about fifteen million tons a year.

Energy saved is quantified with the concept of negawatts – 'fewer watts'. For example, by using an energy-saving twenty-watt bulb instead of a classic incandescent eighty-watt one, you gain sixty negawatts.

IF ALL EUROPEAN UNION CITIZENS REPLACED THEIR INCANDESCENT LIGHT BULBS WITH ENERGY-SAVING BULBS THEY WOULD REDUCE CO₂ EMISSIONS BY ABOUT FIFTEEN MILLION TONS A YEAR.

Energy efficiency has already proven it works on a large scale. Indeed, during the clashes over oil in the 1970s, France, like many other countries, successfully established energy-saving policies. From 1973 to 1987, one hundred billion francs (fifteen billion euros) were invested in energy efficiency. This saved almost as much energy as the French nuclear program produced – which cost five times as much.

Energy that is saved is financially profitable. In a lot of cases, it even makes money. By 2020, it could save member countries of the Organisation for Economic Cooperation and Development (OCDE) over one hundred billion euros. However, this path has not been explored as it means lower consumption and production compared to the usual targets, which are ever more demanding.

See also pages 170, 174 and 186.

New Songdo City Development, South Korea (37°23'N, 126°40'E). The Songdo International Business District is located forty kilometres southeast of South Korea's capital, Seoul. It is an immense building project on a 607-hectare polder. The city was designed to be one of the greenest in the world and sets a good example on issues such as energy saving, public transportation and waste management.

NUCLEAR POWER

For a while, nuclear power was pushed to the side because of negative public opinion and high investment costs. In the past few years though, it has been given a new lease of life: thirty-six reactors are currently being built and about one hundred more are planned. In 2008, 439 nuclear reactors were active, providing 6.3 per cent of the world's electricity.

This revival is due to relative energy shortages and the fact that nuclear power emits very little CO_2 into the atmosphere. Building infrastructures, extracting, transporting and enriching fuel may generate greenhouse gases, but the sector's carbon assessment is much better than for fossil fuels. However, on a planetary level, nuclear energy only represents a small amount of the energy that is produced: it could generate up to 18 per cent of the world's electricity, but this only represents a small percentage of global energy production. It is therefore not a solution to the problem. Moreover, uranium resources – the fuel most commonly used by power stations – are not unlimited. According to the IAEA, existing resources are enough to supply the world's reactors for another century, and new deposits could be discovered. But this depends on whether or not the number of reactors increases. Unless, perhaps, future reactors use more readily available fuel.

However, the Chernobyl disaster in 1986 showed that accidents can indeed happen. Extracting uranium can also be dangerous for miners and the environment. We still do not know what to do with radioactive waste, and the risk of proliferation or attack is omnipresent.

How can we balance the pros and cons of nuclear energy? Some countries have asked their citizens using referendums. However, in other countries, like France – where 78 per cent of electricity comes from nuclear energy –, the involvement in the civil nuclear industry was unilaterally decided by the government.

See also pages 92, 116 and 160.

> NUCLEAR POWER HAS BEEN GIVEN A NEW LEASE OF LIFE. IN 2008, 439 NUCLEAR REACTORS WERE ACTIVE, PROVIDING 6.3 PER CENT OF THE WORLD'S ELECTRICITY.

Tailings at the Arlit uranium mine, Niger (19°00'N, 7°38'E). Some three thousand tons of uranium are extracted from the Arlit Mine every year – about 8 per cent of world production. The exploitation of a new deposit in Imouraren, Africa's biggest uranium mine, eighty kilometres south of Arlit, should soon begin. Despite its mineral wealth, Niger is still one of the poorest countries in the world.

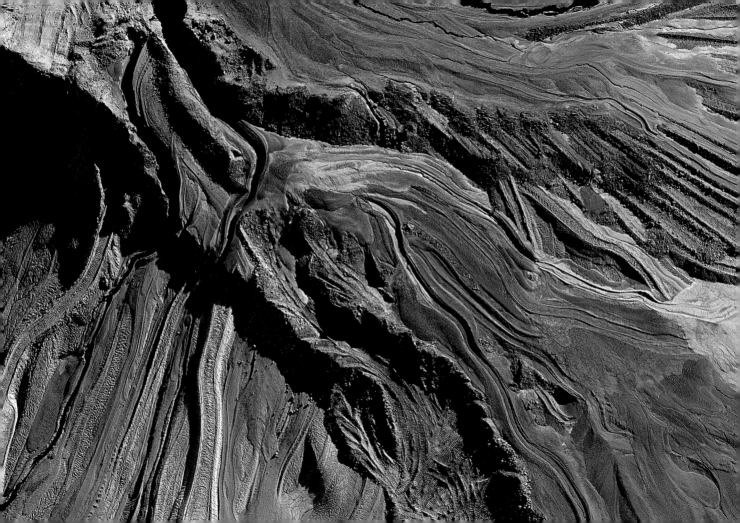

BIOFUELS

Increasing the use of biofuel could reduce CO$_2$ emissions by five hundred million tons a year. In fact, the CO$_2$ biofuels emit as they burn was already circulating in the atmosphere beforehand: it had been absorbed by the plants that were used to make it. There is thus a reduction in the total amount of greenhouse gases that biofuel produces. However, it is a controversial subject.

First, because it requires energy to produce fertilizers, pesticides, agricultural equipment, all needed to make biofuels. In some cases, like for sugar cane alcohol, this is insignificant. However, it is not the case for corn-based ethanol, the United States' main biofuel. It sometimes generates less energy than the amount required to produce it.

Second, in some countries producing biofuels causes large amounts of deforestation. Most of the deforestation in Indonesia and Malaysia is due to oil palm plantations, some of which are used for biofuel. This deforestation emits large amounts of greenhouse gases.

Lastly, some plants used for biofuel are grown on increasingly scarce land that could be used to grow food. We have to choose between feeding people or feeding engines! Indeed, all the cultivated land in the world is not enough to produce sufficient fuel for our almost two billion cars!

To solve these problems, specialists are trying to develop new second-generation biofuels. These are made out of inedible parts of plants, straw, wood, and plants that can grow on poor soil. In the meantime, we must remember that CO$_2$ emissions could be reduced even further by making existing vehicles more fuel efficient.

See also pages 40, 72 and 110.

SOME PLANTS USED FOR BIOFUEL ARE GROWN ON INCREASINGLY SCARCE LAND THAT COULD BE USED TO GROW FOOD.

Doe walking through a rapeseed field in the Chevreuse valley, France (48°50'N, 1°47'E). Cultivating rapeseed for biofuel has been privileged in France because it makes it possible to use fallow land. Governments objectives estimate that 27.5 million hectolitres of ester will be made from rapeseed in 2010 compared to the approximately nine million hectolitres of ethanol that will be made from wheat and sugar beets.

GEOTHERMAL POWER

You don't have to live in Iceland to enjoy the benefits of geothermal energy, which can be used for hydrotherapy, electricity or heating greenhouses. In the centre of Paris, some buildings (such as the Maison de la radio) are heated this way and there isn't a volcano in sight! This is also the case in the United States, New Zealand and the Philippines. All around the world, there is heat below the ground. The closer you get to the central core (4000°C), the hotter it is: the temperature rises by an average of 3°C every one hundred metres.

This heat source is used in different ways. High-temperature geothermal systems produce electricity in geothermal power plants. By drilling down to five hundred metres, it is possible to reach water vapour that is trapped in the subsoil at temperatures of 150 to 350°C. This powers a turbine that in turn produces electricity. There are plenty of geothermal resources that can be used for electricity production in the Pacific (28 per cent of geo-thermal electricity is produced in the Philippines), Russia, and Central and Eastern Europe, but on a global scale, geothermal energy accounts for less than 1 per cent of electricity needs.

> OUR OWN PLANET IS OFFERING CLEAN, RENEWABLE ENERGY THAT IS ALWAYS AVAILABLE AND DOES NOT DESTABILIZE THE CLIMATE.

Low-temperature geothermal systems, meanwhile, are used to produce heat. Hot water (between 20°C and 150°C) that circulates deep in the permeable rock is sucked up and used to heat houses, buildings, agricultural greenhouses and piscicultural basins. There are also very low-temperature geothermal systems that use heat stored in near-surface soil to provide air conditioning and supply hot water to individual houses.

Today's technology is advanced enough to develop this energy, which has not yet reached its full potential. Our own planet is offering clean, renewable energy that is always available and does not destabilize the climate.
See also pages 92, 112 and 114.

Geothermal power plant near the Reykjanes Lighthouse, Iceland (63°50'N, 22°41'W). The Reykjanes Peninsula is in a volcanic region with many natural hot springs. Molten magma heats water two thousand metres underground to a temperature of 240°C. By the time the water reaches the surface, the temperature is 70°C. In Iceland, geothermal energy supplies heating for 87 per cent of the population and produces 26 per cent of the electricity.

NEW CITIES

The sector in which greenhouse gas emissions could be most reduced is housing. By 2020, emissions could be cut by 29 per cent. This would not cost much because technical solutions already exist. Double-glazed windows reduce heat loss by 15 to 20 per cent. Lights that go off when the room is empty, energy-saving bulbs and a better use of natural light could reduce energy consumption linked to domestic lighting by 75 per cent. Every year, this emits 1.9 gigatons of CO_2.

Extremely simple steps can bring about surprisingly significant changes. On a planetary scale, whitening all roofs would reduce CO_2 emissions by forty-four billion tons. White roofs would reflect more energy into space and reduce the number of warming infrared rays. Alternately, covering them with vegetation would provide better insulation.

Another major urban issue is transportation. We can reduce pollution by developing motors that consume less and run on alternative fuels or electricity. But for better mobility, urban planning itself must be rethought. Green neighbourhoods, like Vauban in Freiburg, Germany, and the BedZED development in London, England, provide examples of how to live without cars. Fifty per cent of all car trips are less than five kilometres long, especially in Europe. In most cases, people could walk, ride a bicycle or use public transportation.

Today, these green neighbourhoods, or eco-quarters, are still isolated initiatives on a small scale, because cities develop slowly. Urban policies need time to be applied. Houses have a long lifespan and building professionals are not always trained to use new techniques. But cost is not usually a determining factor, as governments often offer subsidies and savings make up for the extra expenditure.

See also pages 42, 66 and 180.

> FIFTY PER CENT OF ALL CAR TRIPS ARE LESS THAN FIVE KILOMETRES LONG, ESPECIALLY IN EUROPE. IN MOST CASES, PEOPLE COULD WALK, RIDE A BICYCLE OR USE PUBLIC TRANSPORTATION.

Vauban eco-quarter in Freiburg im Breisgau, Baden-Württemberg, Germany (47°59'N, 7°49'E). In the 1970s, Freiburg's population mobilised against the construction of a regional nuclear power station and chose instead to use renewable energy. In 1992, the French army pulled out of the town's military base, which made it possible to develop the Vauban eco-quarter. The houses were built with renewable materials and the roofs are covered in vegetation.

AGRICULTURAL PRACTICES

Even in the countryside it is possible to fight the greenhouse effect. Indeed, changing agricultural practices can reduce carbon dioxide emissions by billions of tons. And this can often be done using simple means.

Increasing the carbon storage capacity of soil is the main change that can be made. The variety of crops makes it difficult to suggest a common method, but this can involve restoring degraded soil by regularly mulching it in winter or protecting it through reforestation. It can also mean reducing ploughing, which affects the quality and quantity of organic matter in the topsoil. Interest has once again arisen in traditional practices like *terra preta* (black earth), also known as biochar. A type of charcoal made of organic matter, it is added to the earth and acts as both a filter and a pesticide. Most importantly, it can also store CO_2.

It is also possible to reduce agricultural greenhouse gas emissions by restricting the use of nitrogen fertilizers – the most common source of the greenhouse gas nitrous oxide (N_2O). This can be done through crop rotation, composting and using green, nonpolluting fertilizers. Combining cereal crops with plants like clover, alfalfa (lucerne) and beans, which fix the air's nitrogen in the soil, is another solution. Direct emissions of various greenhouse gases (e.g. methane) from livestock can be reduced by changing the food supply and how manure and pastures are used. Similarly, by drying out rice paddies once or twice a year, methane from rice-growing can be reduced by 80 per cent.

In any case, it is not a matter of using technology or undertaking huge projects. Most of these solutions are financially profitable. But people have to change their practices in both urban and rural areas.

See also pages 40, 72 and 122.

MOST OF THESE SOLUTIONS ARE FINANCIALLY PROFITABLE. BUT PEOPLE HAVE TO CHANGE THEIR PRACTICES IN BOTH URBAN AND RURAL AREAS.

Women drying rice in the sun, Milyang, South Korea (35°27'N, 128°46'E). Thanks to a sharp increase in rice production, South Korea no longer suffers from the famines that once plagued the country prior to the 1960s. The number of surfaces covered with rice paddies throughout the world could rise by 4 per cent by 2030 and even higher for those that are permanently irrigated. This would increase related methane emissions by 16 per cent.

WOOD FUEL

Wood accounts for only 10 per cent of the world's primary energy consumption, but this percentage could be higher. If trees were harvested sustainably – unlike what happens during deforestation - wood would be a renewable resource that does not contribute to global warming.

It is all a matter of rhythm. A forest is composed of standing carbon that renews itself as trees and other vegetation grow (when they trap CO_2) and die (when they release CO_2). When a forest is mature, the life cycle is balanced. If wood is cut down and burned, the CO_2 that is released is compensated for by the growth of other trees. Thus, burning wood from sustainably managed forests is carbon neutral.

Unlike in the rest of the world, European and North American forest cover has been increasing for several decades. European forests are growing by 764 million cubic metres a year. Yet, only 60 per cent of this forest is used as a resource. This is an area that has a high development potential.

IF TREES WERE HARVESTED SUSTAINABLY, WOOD WOULD BE A RENEWABLE RESOURCE THAT DOES NOT CONTRIBUTE TO GLOBAL WARMING.

Even though it is overlooked in developed countries, wood has several advantages. It is produced locally at little cost and provides jobs in rural areas. It increases energy independence. It can be used to produce heat, electricity and fuel for transport or biomaterials (that can be recycled and turned into energy once used). Wood can be burned as is or turned into gas or petrol.

However, burning wood emits many atmospheric pollutants that are unhealthy in a domestic environnement: soot particles, dioxins, furan, PCBs, benzene and lead. This is something that must be considered if the sector is to develop.

See also pages 44, 46 and 102.

Charcoal oven in Carolina, South Africa (26°04'S, 30°06'E). Mpumalanga Province, in the northeast of the country, has many coal deposits that are exploited for industry, electricity and export. Charcoal production, in comparison, is for the local market. Two-thirds of the world's wood fuel is used in developing countries.

CARBON STORAGE

What if we sent carbon back to where it came from - underground? The idea may sound strange, but the practice of capturing and storing CO_2 is something that already exists. It could reduce our emissions by 15 to 55 per cent!

For the past ten years, the Sleipner offshore platform, off the coast of Norway, has been using this process. It captures CO_2 from the exploitation of natural gas and puts it back into permeable rocks about one thousand metres below the sea floor. About one million tons of CO_2 are 'neutralized' in this way every year. There are similar installations, still in the experimental stage, in Denmark, Algeria and Canada.

It is a complex process. To start with, the CO_2 must be separated from other gases. This stage requires heavy equipment and can only be carried out at industrial sites that emit large amounts of CO_2, like power plants. Then, the gas has to be transferred to a geological reservoir. This can simply be an empty oil or gas deposit.

But the gas must not escape. This would negate the benefits in addition to endangering populations. Although CO_2 is not toxic, it can asphyxiate living things. This happened in Cameroon in 1986: Lake Nyos, a natural carbon reservoir, released a large cloud of CO_2 after a landslide, killing over one thousand people instantly. Carbon storage sites must therefore be chosen carefully and constantly monitored.

These reasons explain why carbon storage is expensive. It is only profitable if the price of oil exceeds a certain amount or if an international CO_2 emissions market develops and the ton of CO_2 reaches a certain amount. In any case, this will mean an increase in the price of energy.

See also pages 44, 114 and 116.

> # THE PRACTICE OF CAPTURING AND STORING CO_2 IS SOMETHING THAT ALREADY EXISTS. IT COULD REDUCE OUR EMISSIONS BY 15 TO 55 PER CENT!

Al-Shaheen Ad oil rig, Qatar (25°30'N, 51°30'E). Gas flaring is used to burn off natural gases in oil deposits, because exploiting them is not profitable. Every year, flares waste 150 billion cubic metres of gas. This is the equivalent of 390 million tons of greenhouse gas or 2 per cent of all greenhouse gas emissions.

GEOENGINEERING

If humans can have a negative effect on the climate, perhaps we can have a positive effect on it as well. This is the starting point of geoengineering, which usually involves large scale futuristic projects that seek to transform our planet.

A space sunshade for the Earth - or, more exactly, billions of lenses or tiny metal screens to deflect some of the sun's rays - has been suggested. Reducing the amount of sunlight by 2 per cent would compensate for global warming by 2100.

The eruption of Mount Pinatubo in the Philippines reduced temperature on land by 1.5 per cent in 1991 after severe sulphur emissions. Some people suggested recreating this effect with sulphur and other particles. However, sending sulphur - a very reactive element - into the upper atmosphere causes problems. Clouds of sea water could produce the same effect but one would have to project ten thousand litres of water per second to form enough cloud cover to compensate for global warming.

PLAYING GOD WITH OUR PLANET COULD HAVE UNPREDICTABLE SECONDARY EFFECTS.

Feeding phytoplankton with iron sulphates or nitrogen fertilizers could increase the amount of CO_2 captured by oceans. This is the only bioengineering solution for which exterior testing has been carried out. But the results are disappointing. Some studies show that this addition will increase the number of phytoplankton by 30 per cent, which then absorb more CO_2, but in the end, very little CO_2 is stored.

Those who see these ideas as ways of playing God fear the solution may be worse than the problem, because directly changing our planet could have unpredictable secondary effects. Such action is part of an 'engineering' viewpoint that considers the environment should be transformed, rather than seeking to restore the existing natural balance.

See also pages 92, 98 and 116.

Islets and seabed, Exuma Cays, Bahamas (24°28'N, 76°46'W). The Bahamas archipelago, southeast of Florida and north of Haiti and Cuba, is made up of over seven hundred coral islands. The clear water here is home to one of the world's richest deep-sea environments. Ocean life captures billions of tons of carbon every year. However, up until now attempts to widen the extent of this phenomenon have failed.

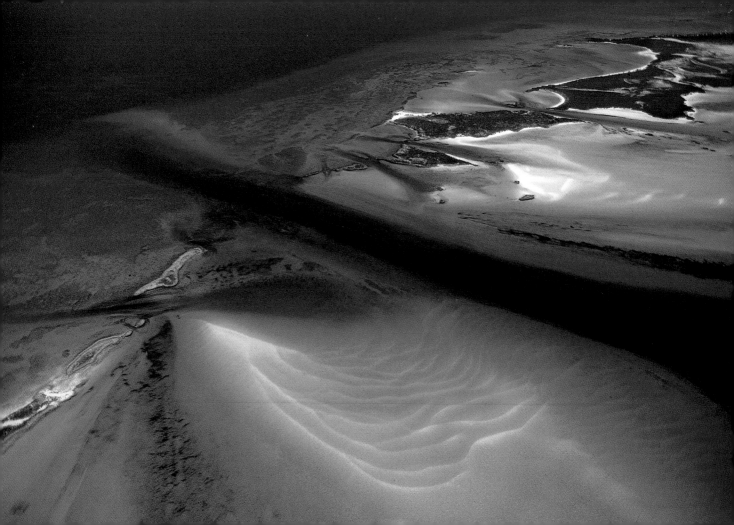

OPTIMISM

There's no need to worry about climate change, because researchers will find a solution to the problem, right? But even for those who have an unshakeable faith in scientific progress, time is an obstacle. In some ways, it's like cancer: there's no need to stop smoking since doctors will eventually find a cure. Of course, it might take scientists a few decades or centuries to find a cure, and every year, lung cancer kills over one million people.

Nuclear fusion, clean energy, biofuel made from algae, new carbon-storing technology – there are many possibilities. If scientists manage to invent all of this in addition to other methods of reducing our greenhouse gas emissions, it will be great news. But we are running out of time – the climate may warm up by over 2°C in the coming decades. If this is indeed the case, the planet's different balances could be disturbed, maybe irreversibly. We can't sit back and wait for scientific progress and its unpredictable development.

> TECHNOLOGICAL PROGRESS IS ALREADY TAKEN INTO ACCOUNT IN ALL SCENARIOS. IT COULD REDUCE CO_2 EMISSIONS BY SEVERAL THOUSAND BILLION TONS OVER A CENTURY!

In fact, technological progress is already taken into account in all scenarios. It could reduce CO_2 emissions by several thousand billion tons over a century! But even in the most optimistic scenario, it alone will not eliminate the problem. The remaining reductions will have to be made through social measures we won't be able to avoid.

We cannot separate technological progress from financial and social issues. Indeed, most of the necessary technology already exists on an experimental basis, but it is seldom (or even never) used, because it is too expensive. Reducing costs or finding a way to make it affordable – through subsidies, for example – is not easy. Technology might therefore cost much more than we think.

See also pages 114, 122 and 168.

Qatar Science and Technology Park, Doha, Qatar (25°19'N, 51°26'E). On the roof of the Qatar Science and Technology Park, traditional Islamic designs are mixed with the Japanese architect Arata Isozaki's clean lines. Qatar is taking advantage of revenue from its abundant oil and gas resources to invest in a high-level university program for the future. The country has the highest greenhouse gas emissions per inhabitant.

PROTECTING LIFE

Our efforts to protect nature have not been enough to stop the extinction of many species. Global warming has made things even more complicated: we need new strategies to protect the planet's biodiversity.

Ecosystems are changing and species are migrating. One solution is to enlarge protected areas, an argument in favour of large transnational reserves. Panama, Ecuador, Costa Rica and Columbia have reached an agreement to manage the marine species that migrate in their waters. Larger protected areas are often more diverse, which makes it easier for living organisms to find the specific conditions that best suit them. They also make it possible to support larger populations that are more genetically diverse and more viable.

Ecological corridors can be created to allow animals and vegetation to extend from one habitat to another, without being blocked by artificial zones. A 2,800-kilometre corridor

> ECOSYSTEMS ARE CHANGING AND SPECIES ARE MIGRATING. ONE SOLUTION IS TO ENLARGE PROTECTED AREAS, AN ARGUMENT IN FAVOUR OF LARGE TRANSNATIONAL RESERVES.

specially dedicated to climate change has been set up in Australia; it helps certain species adapt and survive.

Alternately, protection can be adapted as species migrate and gradually change the limits of existing protected areas: these would be mobile reserves. This new idea is hard to set up as delimiting protected areas is a slow and complex process.

If all this fails, in the future many species will only exist in museums, seed banks or zoos. But even this solution is not satisfactory. For example, there are many polar bears in zoos throughout the world, but as a large predator with an immense territorial habitat, it does not fare well in confined spaces. Usually, nature cannot be put in a jar.

See also pages 22, 26 and 74.

Humpback whale in Samana Bay, Dominican Republic (18°20'N, 69°50'W). Whales are migratory marine mammals. They spend the summer in the Arctic and swim south in the winter to give birth. Despite the 1986 ban on commercial whaling and the creation of the Southern Ocean Whale Sanctuary in 1994, countries like Japan and Norway have not stopped whaling.

LESSONS FROM THE HEAT WAVE

The heat wave that struck Europe in August 2003 is an example of a health disaster that led to adaptation measures on several levels. Almost fifteen thousand people died in France; about thirty-five thousand people died in the rest of Europe. One of the world's most developed areas was devastated over a two-week period by an exceptional heat wave.

Hospitals and clinics were overflowing with people. The state was slow to assess the situation and react, and there was little communication between the different branches of government. The crisis was even more serious than it had to be because it had not been anticipated. Even with temperatures that were 5°C above average for two weeks, it was no hotter in Paris than it normally is during summer in Rio de Janeiro!

As a result, the French government set up a 'national heat-wave plan' the following summer. The authorities made the population aware of the dangers and improved care for the elderly. Hospital and retirement-home structures were improved with the installation of ventilation and air conditioning. If government figures are to be believed, this has been beneficial: according to estimates, a milder heat wave in France in 2006 would have, without these preventive measures, killed 6,500 people. It 'only' killed two thousand people.

Heat waves are only one example of phenomena that will become more frequent because of global warming. Infectious diseases, droughts and storms will test our resiliency. Some of these risks have been identified. It is thus also possible to partly protect yourself. Malaria awareness and prevention campaigns, improved storm surveillance and flood prevention are already necessary.

See also pages 18, 78 and 168.

EVEN WITH TEMPERATURES THAT WERE 5°C ABOVE AVERAGE FOR TWO WEEKS, IT WAS NO HOTTER IN PARIS THAN IT NORMALLY IS DURING SUMMER IN RIO DE JANEIRO!

Saint-Aygulf Beach, between Saint-Raphaël and Fréjus, French Riviera, France (43°24'N, 6°44'E). Saint-Raphaël and Fréjus were tiny fishing villages at the beginning of the twentieth century, but they are now fashionable destinations for sunbathers. But the price of tanned skin can be high: skin cancer is increasingly frequent in most parts of the world. In France, the number of cases doubles every ten years.

TRADITIONAL KNOWLEDGE

Adaptation to the natural environment is one of the keys to humanity's very existence. Today, traditional practices are being revived so that we can adapt better to climate change.

In India, for example, Rajendra Singh and his NGO, Tarun Bharat Sangh (The Young India Association), have revived dozens of rivers that had dried up in Rajasthan by building *johads*, traditional cisterns built with mud and rocks. These huge water reserves, rediscovered by this 'river maker', make it possible to supply water to Indian villages threatened by desertification.

Ten centuries ago, pre-Colombian civilizations in South America that depended on climate variations for their harvest developed engineering marvels to channel and store rain water and melt-off from Andean glaciers. Some of these canals are still working today.

In Australia, traditional forest fire management preserved the region's biodiversity. This type of land management disappeared after the Aborigines were forced off their land. But today, park rangers are approaching them to again set up such systems and protect threatened species.

In Egypt, arc-shaped bambo roofs in rural villages are inspired by traditional constructions. These roofs are smaller than flat roofs, making it easier to keep the house cool as hot air rises and cool air stays on the ground's surface. The openings allow natural air-conditioning through cross-ventilation. Other countries use different forms of this technique.

Modern science can help local populations face climate change but traditional techniques have been tested by centuries of experimentation and practice. This knowledge can serve as the starting point of more global solutions.

See also pages 92, 116 and 120.

> *JOHADS*, TRADITIONAL CISTERNS BUILT WITH MUD AND ROCKS, MAKE IT POSSIBLE TO SUPPLY WATER TO INDIAN VILLAGES THREATENED BY DESERTIFICATION.

Oasis in Tichit, Aoukar region, Mauritania (18°00'N, 9°30'W). Mauritania is a large arid country with about three million inhabitants. It is particularly affected by desertification. Thanks to water channelling in the Aoukar region in the middle of the country, the population has been able to cultivate vegetables and date crops in the middle of the desert. Barriers of branches prevent these small oases from silting up.

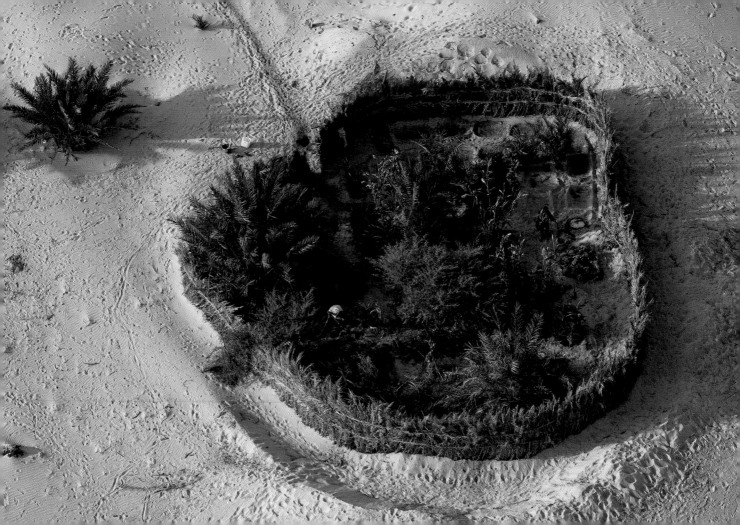

FACING THE PROBLEM

Solutions

Global warming is inevitable. The effects of the phenomenon can already be felt and are going to get progressively worse over the next few decades. Even if energy measures are taken, it will take a long time for them to take effect. We must face the problem and adapt. Currently, the most difficult problem is rising sea levels.

There are three strategies to deal with this: containing the rising waters, adapting to new conditions or retreating. The first means building dykes or improving existing barriers. In the Netherlands, a quarter of the country is below sea level. After a tidal wave struck in 1953, the government began a thirty-year project (the Delta Plan) to stop such a disaster from ever happening again. However, it isn't possible to raise ground levels and build dykes everywhere. It is also very expensive.

The second method is adapting to floods: for example, building raised houses, providing amphibious means of transport, and so on. There aren't many solutions. One thing is sure: seaside developments are not a good investment.

IF SEA LEVELS RISE BY SEVERAL METRES, MANHATTAN WILL BE UNDER WATER. FIFTY PER CENT OF THE WORLD'S POPULATION LIVES LESS THAN SIXTY KILOMETRES FROM THE SEA.

It is not easy to move to higher altitudes when there is no available land. For many people, losing their land or home means poverty unless compensation systems are set up – but this is rarely the case. The Bangladeshis will not be the only casualties: if sea levels rise by several metres, Manhattan will also be under water. Fifty per cent of the world's population lives less than sixty kilometres from the sea.

For the moment, adaptation measures are containing most of the effects of global warming. But they could become insufficient. This is another reason why we must fight both the causes and the effects of global warming.

See also pages 16, 68 and 82.

Tulip field near Lisse, Netherlands (52°15'N, 4°37'E). The Netherlands produce 65 per cent of the world's flower bulbs. But this cultivation was carried out at the environment's expense: in the 1990s, flower bulbs required the most pesticides in all of Europe. Over half of the country's population and economic activity is in areas protected by dykes and dunes.

MONEY MATTERS

Greenhouse gas emissions can be reduced in many ways, but there is a price to pay. The more expensive CO_2 becomes, the more these solutions will become profitable and the more they will be used. The area where the most savings could be made is in construction, and that's even with inexpensive CO_2. The indicated values do not include non-technical options, such as lifestyle changes.

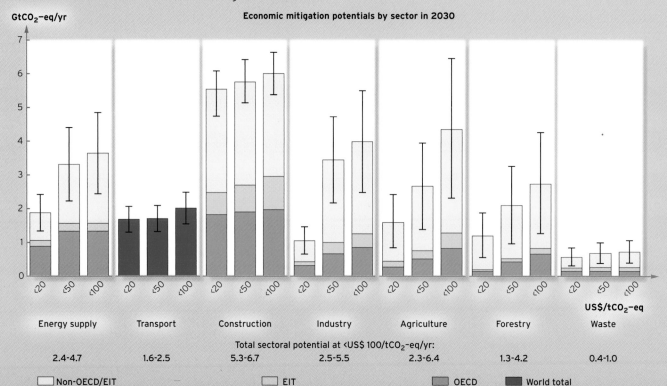

Economic mitigation potentials by sector in 2030

GtCO$_2$–eq/yr

US$/tCO$_2$–eq

Total sectoral potential at <US$ 100/tCO$_2$-eq/yr:

Energy supply	Transport	Construction	Industry	Agriculture	Forestry	Waste
2.4-4.7	1.6-2.5	5.3-6.7	2.5-5.5	2.3-6.4	1.3-4.2	0.4-1.0

Non-OECD/EIT   EIT   OECD   World total

A CARBON-RICH ECONOMY

As the GDP increases, so does our energy consumption and CO_2 emissions. However, this correlation is getting weaker; it takes increasingly less energy to produce a dollar's worth, and increasingly less CO_2 to produce energy: the economy is 'decarbonising'. But the GDP is increasing faster than decarbonisation, so global emissions continue to increase.

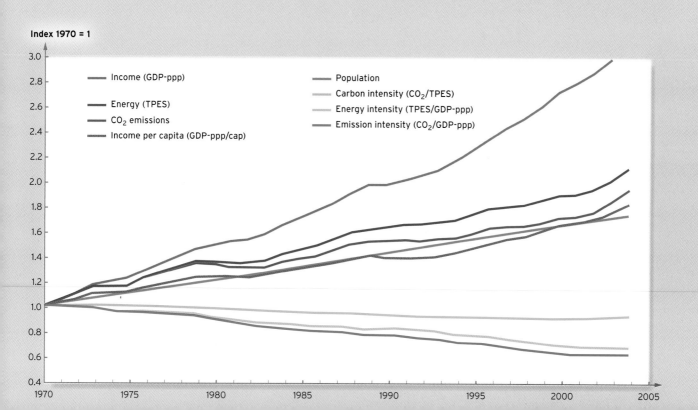

Index 1970 = 1

Legend:
- Income (GDP-ppp)
- Energy (TPES)
- CO_2 emissions
- Income per capita (GDP-ppp/cap)
- Population
- Carbon intensity (CO_2/TPES)
- Energy intensity (TPES/GDP-ppp)
- Emission intensity (CO_2/GDP-ppp)

Sunita, *New Delhi, India*
I have no doubt about people's goodwill to move things forward; I have no doubt that the poor are ready to give some space to the rich. But I am very afraid that the leaders of the world will totally give up on us. I am afraid of the world's faithless leaders. I fear the leaders who are too cowardly to take the strict decisions that the world needs.

Sunita

Yousuf

Aslam, *Maldive Islands*
As a citizen of the Maldives, what I have to say to the world is that we may be among the first to be impacted by climate change, we may be among the first of the countries that will be wiped off the map, but make no mistake – we will not be the last.
If you cannot save us, you know it is just a matter of time before it's your turn.
Save us and you save yourself.

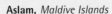
Aslam

Yousuf, *Maldive Islands*
What I want to tell to the West is that we shouldn't be hurt because of their wrong-doings. Then only we can breathe a sigh of relief. Otherwise, if we are not even willing to be partners with them, we will cease to exist anymore if they are not careful. It doesn't matter how many agreements we sign with them, we will exist only if they understand our situation.

Leon, *Texas, United States*
If you don't trust the established powers to bring the necessary change, you should take care of it yourself.

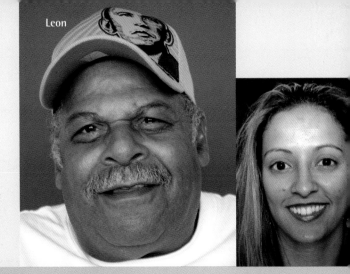

Leon

NEGOTIATIONS

Rosario

Rosario, *south of Spain*
I would like to tell the leaders that they should not forget that they are humans too; the fact that they have power doesn't make them special. They have power because we gave it to them. And they must use their knowledge for everyone's sake.

KYOTO: A FIRST STEP

Despite its importance, the Kyoto Protocol will not have lasted very long. It came about with difficulty in 1997 and then took seven years to be implemented. Now, after having been barely enforced, it is soon going to expire. In 2012, a second treaty will replace it.

The ideas for the protocol were drafted at the 1992 Rio de Janeiro Earth Summit. At the conference, 154 countries adopted the United Nations Framework Convention on Climate Change (the UNFCCC; there are now 192 countries that have adopted it). The principle of the convention is to stabilize the greenhouse gas concentration in the atmosphere. No actual figures were set, but the guidelines for international cooperation were established.

The IPCC experts gradually proved that the phenomenon existed beyond all reasonable doubt. A period of intense negotiations began, culminating in Kyoto, Japan, on 11 December 1997. That day, thirty-eight countries committed themselves to reducing their emissions by 5.2 per cent by 2012. The Kyoto Protocol was born.

However, the United States, at the time responsible for over one-third of the world's emissions, refused to ratify the treaty because it exempted developing nations, from having to meet the same requirements. Unfortunately, the treaty could only take effect if the committed industrialized countries accounted for at least 55 per cent of total emissions. The Kyoto Protocol finally came into effect on 16 February 2005, when Russia agreed to add their 17 per cent of world emissions to the cause.

Even if its creation was fraught with difficulties, its aims were moderate and the results were so disappointing – world emissions have increased since 1990 – Kyoto managed to bring together the world's leaders. It initiated a process that the Copenhagen summit needs to build upon, as years of neglect mean that the problem of climate change needs to be tackled more urgently than ever before.

See also pages 28, 144 et 146.

> KYOTO BROUGHT TOGETHER THE WORLD'S LEADERS AND INITIATED A PROCESS THAT THE COPENHAGEN SUMMIT NEEDS TO BUILD UPON.

The Corcovado overlooking Rio de Janeiro, Brazil (22°57'S, 43°13'W). Atop the 704-metre-high Corcovado Peak ('The Hunchback'), the famous statue of Christ the Redeemer towers above Guanabara Bay and the famous Sugarloaf Mountain. In 1992, the second Earth Summit was organized in Rio. It was during this summit that the resolve to reduce greenhouse gas emissions emerged.

THE FINAL OUTCOME

When the Kyoto Protocol was first signed in 1997, only thirty-eight countries committed themselves to reducing their emissions. These included members of the EU, Japan, Canada, the United States, Russia and Australia. They form Annex I. No limitations were set for other countries. Together, they decided to reduce their total emissions by 5 per cent between 1990 and 2012, and shared the effort among themselves: -8 per cent for Western Europe, -6 per cent for Japan and Eastern European countries, and so on.

Ten years later, there are mixed results: emissions have decreased by 4.7 per cent, mainly thanks to former Soviet Union countries. Their overall emissions decreased by 37 per cent on average over the ten-year period because of a crisis triggered by switching to a market economy. The United States still has not ratified the treaty and Australia only did so in December 2007. Their emissions have increased by 14 per cent and 29 per cent respectively. The emissions of Spain,

THE KYOTO PROTOCOL DEPENDED UPON VOLUNTARY ACTION, AND THEREFORE DID NOT SUGGEST ANY WAYS OF SANCTIONING THOSE WHO FAILED TO MEET THEIR TARGETS.

Portugal, Greece and Ireland have increased because of strong economic growth over the past twenty years. The emissions of New Zealand and Canada have increased because mineral resources are being exploited. Meanwhile, France has about reached its target and Germany and the United Kingdom have reduced their emissions by over 15 per cent, thanks to policies that favour renewable energy and a reduction in industrial activity.

In spite of all this, the Kyoto Protocol marked an important step in international climate negotiations by setting quantified emission reduction targets. The main treaty is part of the UNFCCC, which only mentioned vague objectives. The limited result is partly explained by the fact that the Kyoto Protocol depended upon voluntary action, and therefore did not suggest any ways of sanctioning those who failed to meet their targets. However, this might change with the next treaty.

See also pages 134, 150 and 166.

Building a golf course in Cap Cana, Dominican Republic (18°27'N, 68°25'W). This golf course is aimed at wealthy tourists and is part of a huge resort that spreads for dozens of miles along a sandy beach in the Caribbean. The world's twenty richest countries are responsible for 80 per cent of all greenhouse gas emissions.

THE REST OF THE WORLD

Most countries that are signatories of the Kyoto Protocol have not committed to anything, or, more accurately, they do not have to reduce their emissions. Only thirty-eight out of 186 signatory countries committed themselves to meeting actual targets. The others were grouped together in the 'non-annex I' category: they calculate their emissions and send the information to the United Nations. And that's about it.

The nations that are on this 'non-annex I' list have varied and sometimes contradictory interests. OPEC member countries that export oil and are big emitters ratified the Kyoto Protocol. AOSIS (Alliance of Small Island States) member countries (e.g. the Maldives, Tuvalu), which are directly threatened by rising sea levels, did the same. Dozens of developing countries also ratified the protocol, but the term can refer to both very poor countries, like Mali, as well as emerging economic powers such as China, India and Brazil.

IF THE MOST DEVELOPED COUNTRIES SET AN EXAMPLE BY REDUCING THEIR OWN GREENHOUSE GAS EMISSIONS, OTHERS WILL GRADUALLY FOLLOW THEIR LEAD.

Why are so many states part of the Kyoto Protocol, even if they have not committed themselves to reducing their greenhouse gas emissions? Making them take part in the debates and negotiations is a way of getting them involved. Moreover, signatory states have to keep national emissions registers. They have to set up procedures to estimate emissions, the first step in reducing them.

The idea is to set off a chain reaction: if the most developed countries set an example by reducing their own greenhouse gas emissions, others will gradually follow their lead. Convincing countries that have not yet made a commitment to make one will be a major issue in future negotiations, especially as the emissions of non-annex I countries, led by China and India, have increased considerably. They accounted for less than half the emissions in 1990, now represent about 70 per cent of the current total, and are continuing to increase. *See also pages 140, 150 and 182.*

Fly ash deposits, Mpumalaga province, South Africa (26°31'S, 29°07'E). These huge central reservations are made up of ash produced by a factory that turns coal into liquid hydrocarbon. The factory alone covers an area of thirteen square kilometres. Producing one litre of fuel through this process emits double the amount of greenhouse gas as producing the equivalent amount with oil.

THE UNITED STATES

The United States is one of the world's biggest polluter per capita. Despite this, it never ratified the Kyoto Protocol. Although Al Gore symbolically signed the treaty in 1998 when he was vice president, in 1997 the US Senate had already voted unanimously against signing any climate agreement that exempted developing nations from having to meet similar standards.

Over the course of the next decade, the American government became one of the main obstacles to reaching an agreement in international climate negotiations. The Bush administration, influenced by the 'sceptic' lobbies, denied the reality of climate change and put pressure on scientists who disagreed.

Both Republicans and Democrats were worried that regulations related to global warming would hinder the country's economy. George Bush Sr once declared, 'The American way of life is not up for negotiation'. This point was evoked in the 1997 Senate resolution. The text men-tioned a second point that remains at the heart of the American argument: the United States will refuse to take steps unless other countries are also forced to do so - especially in the emerging economies of China, India and Brazil.

Despite the delay that occurred on a national level during the Bush years, many initiatives have emerged independently in the United States. Some states, like California, have decided to adhere to the Kyoto objectives. Over nine hundred American cities, including New York, Los Angeles and Chicago, as well as many communities and institutions, have done the same thing.

Barack Obama's election in 2008 could mark a turning point in America's environmental policies. After taking office, the new president announced that he wanted to make climate change one of his priorities. However, it is hard to anticipate how far he is willing to go and, more importantly, how far the US Congress is willing to let him go.

See also pages 28, 130 and 150.

> BARACK OBAMA'S ELECTION IN 2008 COULD MARK A TURNING POINT IN AMERICA'S ENVIRONMENTAL POLICIES.

Henderson, Las Vegas suburb, United States (35°60'N, 115°05'W). Las Vegas, the city of excess, is located 450 kilometres northeast of Los Angeles in the middle of the desert. Every year, the population increases by an additional fifty thousand inhabitants. Despite little rainfall (barely more than ten centimetres annually), forty million tourists visit Las Vegas every year. The sprawling development here is typical of North American suburbs.

EMISSION QUOTAS

Each country enacts different measures to reduce emissions in accordance with their targets. There are a variety of possibilities: taxing emissions, subsidizing energy consumption reduction programmes, aiding the development of renewable energy, and so on.

The most important measure is setting emission quotas, which have to decrease over time. The government allows certain large industries to emit limited amounts of greenhouse gas – measured in tons of CO_2. It is easier to control the emissions of the largest emitters at the source: there are a limited number of industrial sites that account for a large share of emissions. Generally, these quotas are assigned, but a portion of them might be sold.

Governments often hesitate to penalize their own industries: they are very generous when allocating quotas, especially during the early stages. Many companies also receive exemptions. Within the European Union, national quota allocation plans were established for 2005-2008 and 2008-2012. But, as an example, when the French government proposed its second plan in 2006, it allowed higher emissions than those recorded for the previous period, and exempted over eight hundred companies. The European Commission rejected the plan. In the United States, the recent vote in favour of a law on air quality gave rise to similar negotiations.

After quotas are in place, a second difficulty arises: making companies respect the quotas and reduce their emissions. Usually, if the quotas are exceeded, extra credits have to be purchased. Companies can also be fined. The Kyoto Protocol did not suggest any means of sanctioning if the targets are exceeded, and it is not surprising that governments rarely enforce the quotas. *See also pages 138, 154 and 176.*

GOVERNMENTS OFTEN HESITATE TO PENALIZE THEIR OWN INDUSTRIES.

Janschwalde Thermal Power Station near Peitz, Germany (51°50'N, 14°27'E). On the edge of former East Germany, Janschwalde is one of ten power stations taking advantage of the largest lignite deposits in Europe, which are near the borders of Germany, Poland, and the Czech Republic. Lignite, a type of coal, produces more carbon dioxide during combustion than any other fossil fuel.

FLEXIBILITY MECHANISMS

In 2008, almost one hundred billion euros were exchanged on the carbon market. This was double the amount exchanged in 2007. It is also twelve times more than in 2005, the year the European emissions market was created. One of the Kyoto Protocol's major innovations was therefore a success.

The market is only one of the protocol's 'flexibility mechanisms', a set of economic tools meant to facilitate the application of the treaty and spread the effort between companies and countries. The reasoning is as follows: it doesn't matter where savings are made; greenhouse gas reductions have the same positive impact regardless. We might as well take action where it is easiest and most profitable.

Theoretically, companies that have exceeded their quotas have to buy the emission rights of the companies that emitted less than planned. This makes it possible to financially reward those who pollute less. This market is also supposed to encourage companies to fund concrete

> IT DOESN'T MATTER WHERE SAVINGS ARE MADE; GREENHOUSE GAS REDUCTIONS HAVE THE SAME POSITIVE IMPACT REGARDLESS.

projects – energy-saving devices, renewable energy – in developing countries, which is known as a Clean Development Mechanism (CDM). If a company reduces greenhouse gas emissions in another country, they are credited as a reduction made in its own country. This type of project also makes technology transfers possible. A similar system exists between countries; this is known as Joint Implementation.

The market's instability is hindering the efficiency of the process because minimal prices per ton of CO_2 and price stability encourage companies to make long-term investments to reduce their emissions. The price depends on many factors including the financial situation. It very much depends on quotas allocated by governments, since they determine whether there is a shortage or affluence. The uncertainty of what will happen after 2012 also affects the market.

See also pages 152, 174 and 176.

Working in a field north of Jodhpur, Rajasthan, India (26°22'N, 73°02'E). Two-thirds of Rajasthan, the second-largest Indian state (342,240 square kilometres), is covered in sandy desert formations. However, irrigation has made it possible to grow millet, sorghum, wheat and barley. India and China are the main beneficiaries of Clean Development Mechanisms (CDM): they receive respectively 25 per cent and 34 per cent of all CDM projects.

THE COPENHAGEN CONFERENCE

What will happen in Copenhagen? To get an idea, you have to remember that the Kyoto Protocol is part of the United Nations Framework Convention on Climate Change (UNFCCC). The convention was signed by the 192 United Nations Member States and it is a treaty with an almost universal impact.

Every year, the signatory members (parties) meet. This meeting is called the Conference of the Parties (COP). Each COP has a number. After the treaty came into force in 1994 (two years after it was signed), the first meeting, or COP1, took place in 1995 in Berlin. The most recent meeting, COP14, was held in December 2008 in Poland. In 2009, COP15 takes place in Copenhagen. COPs bring together members of the UNFCCC; not just countries that ratified the Kyoto Protocol. This is why all countries recognized by the UN send their representatives.

Between COPs, negotiators are busy: many meetings are organized between experts and ambassadors, to make progress on certain stumbling blocks. But a COP is an important event. The most important delegates of the signatory states attend; sometimes even presidents or prime ministers attend as well. During the general assembly, when decisions are made, voting takes place - each country has one vote.

How can an agreement be reached? Some governments think that accepting a reduction in their emissions would not be in their best interests - this is the case of major polluters like China or the United States, for example. Some countries prefer not to get involved in any agreement because that way they can take advantage of reduced emissions without having to bear the cost. The art of negotiation consists of getting something you want in exchange for something that someone else wants. With so many parties, and so many interests, it is particularly difficult.

See also pages 28, 50 and 132.

> THE UNFCCC, SIGNED BY 192 MEMBER STATES, IS A TREATY WITH AN ALMOST UNIVERSAL IMPACT.

The Burj Dubai, United Arab Emirates (25°12′N, 55°16′E). The Burj Dubai, standing at a height of 818 metres, was topped out in January 2009. It is the highest structure ever built and is several hundred metres higher than the world's former tallest building, Taipei 101 in Taiwan, which was 508 metres high. The United Arab Emirates is one of the world's highest greenhouse gas emitters per capita, after Qatar and Bahrain.

THE NOBEL PEACE PRIZE

Proving that global warming exists and that increasing concentrations of greenhouse gases are its origin has required mobilization on a scale never seen before. Thousands of researchers in over one hundred countries have been working on this project for twenty years – and they are still working on it today. This exceptional coordination was organized by the Intergovernmental Panel on Climate Change (IPCC), which was created in 1988 by the World Meteorological Organization and the UN Environment Programme.

The IPCC has two aims. The first is to objectively evaluate scientific, technical and socioeconomic information to understand the risks of global warming. The second is to communicate this information to the decision makers – especially representatives of United Nations member states.

The IPCC does not actually conduct any research, but instead synthesizes the work of specialists. It publishes two kinds of documents. The first kind consists of

> THOUSANDS OF RESEARCHERS IN OVER ONE HUNDRED COUNTRIES HAVE BEEN WORKING ON THIS PROJECT FOR TWENTY YEARS – AND THEY ARE STILL WORKING ON IT TODAY.

specialized scientific articles called summary reports. The most recent report was made up of three one-thousand-page volumes. The second kind are known as 'summary for policy makers'. These are about ten pages long and the representatives of the member states vote on them. Each word is weighed, and hours can be spent debating whether one should write 'very likely' or 'virtually certain'.

The work of the IPCC played a major role in international climate negotiations by providing a scientific base. The first evaluation report was published in 1990 for the Rio Earth summit. The second was published in 1995 just before the Kyoto summit. The third was extremely important in the fight against sceptics. The fourth report, published in 2007, serves as a reference in the current post-Kyoto negotiations. Because of their decisive influence, the IPCC was awarded the Nobel Peace Prize in 2007.

See also pages 28, 50 and 132.

Ice tongue entering the Beacon Valley, Taylor Glacier, Dry Valleys, Antarctica (77°48'S, 160°50'E). Antarctica is an immense frozen land, one and a half times the size of Europe. The Dry Valleys region is one of the few areas in Antarctica that is not covered in ice. Scientists' work on the continent has contributed significantly to our understanding of how the planet's climate has evolved.

A PIVOTAL YEAR

The year 2012, when the Kyoto Protocol will expire, is right around the corner. A new agreement on greenhouse gas emissions will have to be found, at least for the 2013-2017 period. But what will the post-Kyoto protocol be like? This is what is being discussed during the international negotiations that have already begun.

Negotiations are running behind schedule because diplomats made few decisions before 2008, preferring to wait for a new US administration that would be more amenable to tackling the problem. This is why the Copenhagen summit in December 2009 is seen as the last chance to reach an agreement before the Kyoto Protocol expires.

What commitments will be made and what concrete tools will be used to make sure they are kept? What restrictive measures will be put in place? This is another major issue since the United Nations Framework Convention on Climate Change does not set any real targets.

THE COPENHAGEN SUMMIT IS THE LAST CHANCE TO REACH AN AGREEMENT BEFORE THE KYOTO PROTOCOL EXPIRES.

Many questions remain unanswered: will big industrialized countries commit themselves to reducing their emissions again? Will they agree to increase their efforts as is necessary? Will the United States finally make a commitment? Will emerging powers such as China and India accept capping their emissions? How will the fight against deforestation be funded? How will the proper functioning of the CO_2 market be ensured? How will developing countries be involved and how will a technology transfer be encouraged?

And what will happen if the talks fail? It is possible that no agreement will be signed, or that a weak agreement, with few concrete commitments, will be the only outcome. In this case, a lot of energy will have been wasted. But global warming will continue to get worse every day, and the need to take action will become even more palpable.

See also pages 148, 166 and 168.

Eroded iceberg in the Unartoq Fjord, Greenland (60°28'N, 45°19'W). Ice here was formed through the accumulation of one hundred thousand years of snowfall; it covers 82 per cent of the big island. Every spring and summer, deep in the fjords, the glaciers calve. This means that as they move forward, they loosen blocks of ice because of the movements of the sea swell and the tides. Because of global warming, Greenland's ice cap is melting faster and faster.

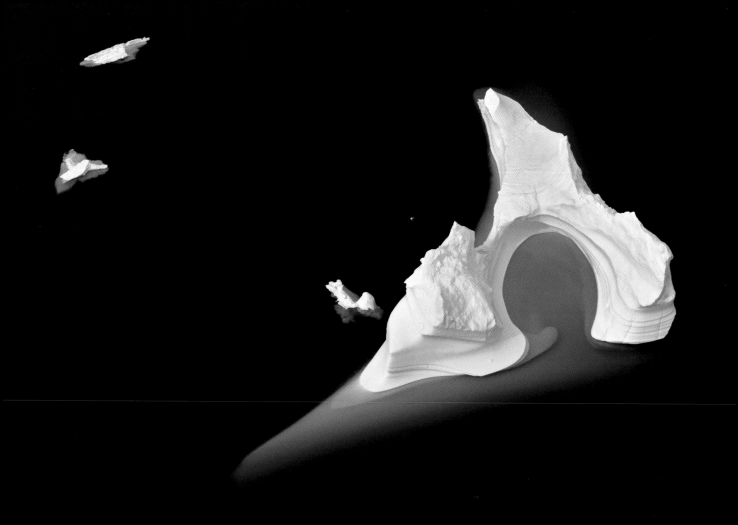

WHICH TARGET?

Which target are we aiming for: 2°C, 350 ppm, 450 ppm, 50 per cent of all carbon emissions? Different global warming limitation targets are often referred to, but what do they really mean?

Limiting an average temperature increase to 2°C (compared to the preindustrial period) is the objective that is most talked about – because it is the most concrete. If we exceed a 2°C increase in temperature, the climate's most important balances will probably be severely and irreversibly disrupted.

In fact, the other figures all refer to the same target. The two ppm values (350 and 450) are equal: the first refers to CO_2 concentration; the second refers to CO_2 concentration plus the equivalent of other greenhouse gases (e.g. methane, nitrous oxide). They both represent the greenhouse gas concentration that would increase the global temperature by about 2°C. Lastly, the 50 per cent minimum reduction in emissions refers to the minimum needed to limit CO_2 levels to 350 ppm – and therefore limit the temperature increase to 2°C.

> IF WE EXCEED A 2°C INCREASE IN TEMPERATURE, THE CLIMATE'S MOST IMPORTANT BALANCES WILL PROBABLY BE SEVERELY AND IRREVERSIBLY DISRUPTED.

Each of these objectives highlights a different part of the problem. Two degrees is the final target that populations should focus on because it will produce the most effect. Greenhouse gas concentration (in ppm) is a parameter that can be measured in the atmosphere, on a planetary level, by scientists. It makes it possible to keep track of the situation accurately. Governments can also measure emissions in each country: it is likely that emissions will be regulated by an international agreement. This is the case with the Kyoto Protocol and we hope it will be the case with the one that follows it. But we should remember that the CO_2 concentration in the atmosphere is already 387 ppm and is increasing by 2 ppm a year. This is a good indicator of how much effort still needs to be made.

See also pages 12, 34 and 180.

Polygonal soil, Beacon Valley, McMurdo Dry Valleys, Antarctica (77°50′S, 160°50′E). The ice buried deep in the ground freezes and thaws to create this strange mineral tapestry. The bottom of the McMurdo Dry Valleys is one of the only places in Antarctica that is not covered in ice. It is made up of polygonal pieces of soil that look like the cracks of a dried-up pond.

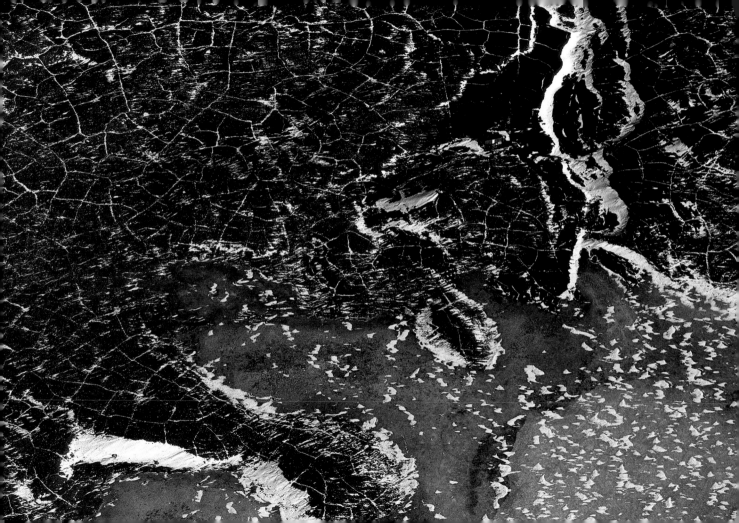

A MATTER OF EQUITY

China is the world's biggest carbon emitter. However, its emissions are not regulated by the protocol. How can China and other emerging powers be convinced that they have to take part in the common effort?

Unlike the Bush administration, the Chinese and Indian governments do not deny the reality of climate change. But they want everyone to play an equal role in the efforts to solve these problems. But how? And based on what?

Emerging economies think it is unfair that they have to make an effort while the most developed countries are not setting the example. They highlight the fact that emissions in the United States – which did not ratify the protocol – rose by 15 per cent between 1990 and 2004. The problem is that the United States is arguing the reverse: they want to ensure that developing countries will take steps against global warming before they agree to anything. So, who will make the first move?

Even if it is accepted that everyone has to get involved, how should the effort be shared? Developing countries claim that throughout history, 77 per cent of the total CO_2 emissions are from developed countries, which means that they should shoulder more responsibility. Then again, emerging countries are emitting more and more CO_2. But per capita, one American still emits five times more CO_2 than one Chinese, and fifteen times more CO_2 than an Indian.

Emerging countries are worried that regulations to reduce greenhouse gas emissions will hinder their economic development, which has greatly reduced poverty and famine (by several hundred million people) in China and India, to mention but two countries. In order for emerging countries to continue their rate of economic development while limiting their emissions, they are asking for a special effort to be made with regard to 'green' technology transfer. This is obviously a delicate subject for the West, as it will encourage the emergence of new economic competitors. *See also pages 86, 132 and 152.*

> EMERGING ECONOMIES THINK IT IS UNFAIR THAT THEY HAVE TO MAKE AN EFFORT WHILE THE MOST DEVELOPED COUNTRIES ARE NOT SETTING THE EXAMPLE.

Waste from a marble quarry near Kishangarh, Rajasthan, India (26°35'N, 74°51'E). Rajasthan is a major marble extraction region and is known for the quality and diversity of its marble. In this region, marble extraction causes serious environmental problems. On a national level, post-1990 economic development has doubled India's greenhouse gas emissions.

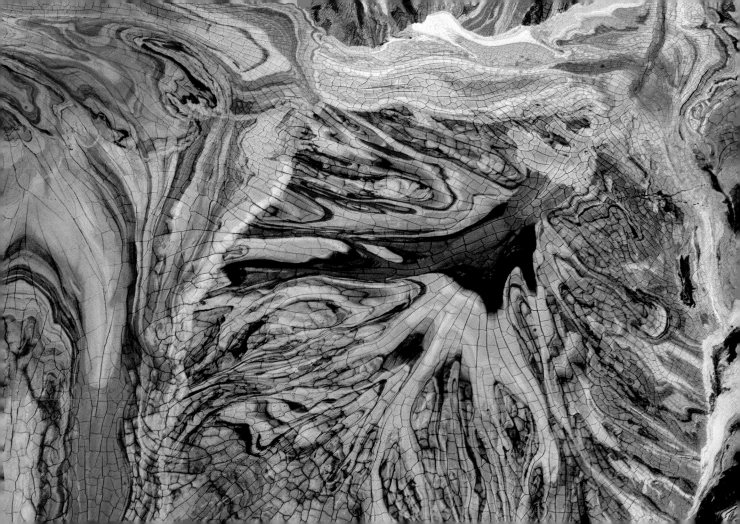

PERSONAL RESPONSIBILITY

What if we completely changed the way of dealing with the problem? The international negotiations dealing with the Kyoto Protocol are at a standstill because governments cannot agree on the necessary efforts. Certain experts have suggested that emissions per person rather than emissions per country should be considered.

This approach makes it possible to overlook transnational rivalries. It makes everyone equally responsible regardless of his or her nationality and makes it possible to take the upper classes in emerging countries into account. Some individuals in emerging countries have standards of living that are similar or superior to their Western counterparts. Within this hypothesis, the determining factor becomes individual wealth, because greenhouse gas emissions tend to increase with the standard of living. This can be overcome: according to certain estimates, limiting the emissions of all human beings to ten tons of CO_2 a year - more than the current European average - would be enough to reduce emissions by 30 per cent by 2030.

> LIMITING THE EMISSIONS OF ALL HUMAN BEINGS TO TEN TONS OF CO_2 A YEAR - MORE THAN THE CURRENT EUROPEAN AVERAGE - WOULD BE ENOUGH TO REDUCE EMISSIONS BY 30 PER CENT BY 2030.

Trial experiments for a personal 'carbon card' are currently being carried out. In the United States and the United Kingdom, certain payment cards already allow people to compensate the emissions linked to their purchases. But there are still many difficulties, especially in evaluating each person's emissions and setting up a system for calculating individual emissions.

This approach makes individuals responsible for the amount of greenhouse gases they emit through consumption, housing and so on. It focuses on behaviour and encourages responsible ways of living. If individual quotas are determined fairly, the system will not penalize the poor, as their emissions are lower. On the contrary, it could even be a way of fighting global warming and poverty at the same time.

See also pages 132, 142 and 150.

Household appliance dump in Aspropyrgos, Greece (38°02'N, 23°35'E). There are about thirty household appliance dumps like this in the Athens region. The components of these products are supposed to be recycled in accordance with the law. But in Greece, in spite of the European Union's environmental objectives, the recycling sector is not very developed.

FIGHTING DEFORESTATION

Deforestation accounts for almost 20 per cent of the world's greenhouse gas emissions. This is more than the United States or the transportation sector. Important international discussions are consequently being held to fight deforestation. These discussions are centred on a mechanism called Reducing Emissions from Deforestation and Degradation (REDD) in developing countries.

The idea is quite unusual since it is a matter of subsidizing deforestation that is avoided. A certain sum of money will be allocated to those who protect forests in proportion to the amount of CO_2 that would have been released into the atmosphere if they had been destroyed.

This will cost an estimated tens of billions of dollars a year. And there are several difficulties. Where will the money come from? The idea is that these funds will more or less come directly from the carbon market, where CO_2 that was not emitted is sold. But the details are the subject of heated debate. Another question: Who gets the money? Most tropical forests are inhabited by indigenous people who have no title deeds. Will they get their share? Who will look out for their interests, which are so often forgotten?

Finally, how can 'avoided deforestation' be calculated? What will act as a reference? If we simply follow current trends it will be problematic, because those who have already cut down a lot of trees, but are now cutting down less than before (like Brazil) will be rewarded more than those who have been making efforts for years and cannot really do anymore (for example, Guyana, which has 76 per cent forest cover).

Even if this financial approach should not substitute for other methods, it gives us hope. Because until now, the other means of fighting deforestation have come up against a lack of institutional capacity, financial resources, and political will. And they have failed.

See also pages 44, 46 and 110.

THIS FINANCIAL APPROACH GIVES US HOPE, BECAUSE UNTIL NOW, THE OTHER MEANS OF FIGHTING DEFORESTATION HAVE FAILED.

Deforestation, Toamasina province, Madagascar (17°05'S, 49°10'E). Madagascar is an island of exceptional biodiversity. About 98 per cent of Madagascar's mammals, 92 per cent of its reptiles and amphibians, and 80 per cent of its plant life is endemic. But this biodiversity is now threatened by extensive deforestation. GoodPlanet is carrying out a five-hundred-thousand-hectare conservation project in conjunction with the WWF and Air France.

THE AIR EXCEPTION

Air travel represents over 2 per cent of CO$_2$ emissions and is rapidly increasing. However, it is not taken into account in climate negotiations. Moreover, airplanes emit nitrogen oxides (NO$_X$) that turn into ozone, a powerful greenhouse gas, at higher altitudes. Because of the altitude conditions and different pressures, the effects of this gas can differ from the effects that can be observed on the ground. In the end, aviation is responsible for 3.5 per cent of greenhouse gas emissions linked to human activity.

Even if the Kyoto Protocol mentions a commitment to limiting or reducing emissions from maritime and air transport, no plans or specific mechanisms are detailed. The main reason for this is that it is hard to determine who is responsible for international transport emissions. To which country should they be attributed: the starting point, the destination, the company, or the passenger or the merchandise?

THE EUROPEAN UNION WILL CALCULATE GREENHOUSE GAS EMISSIONS FROM ALL INTERNATIONAL FLIGHTS DEPARTING FROM OR ARRIVING IN THE EU BEGINNING IN 2012.

What should be done? The European Union has taken the initiative and will calculate greenhouse gas emissions from all international flights departing from or arriving in the EU beginning in 2012. A civil aviation emission-reduction mechanism will be implemented as a market. Companies will be able to buy or sell emission quotas, whose total volume will be brought back to 97 per cent of what they were during the 2003-2006 period.

But it is not just about airplanes. Maritime transport accounts for 89.6 per cent of all shipping – the equivalent of six billion tons a year. Even if ships are still a very energy-efficient means of transport, the distances and huge tonnage explain why their share of CO$_2$ emissions (within the transport sector) is evaluated at 11 per cent. But ships are exempt just like planes. To limit their impact on the environment, one solution would be to relocate economic activities to limit the flow of international merchandise. *See also pages 40, 106 and 184.*

Charles de Gaulle Airport, France (49°00'N, 2°34'E). In 2007, almost sixty million passengers passed through Charles de Gaulle, Europe's second busiest airport. Air transport – mostly carrying people – increases by 5 per cent a year. Jet fuel for international flights is not taxed.

EMISSIONS PER INHABITANT

The average greenhouse gas emission per inhabitant varies from one to ten depending on the continent and geographical group. The United States and Canada are at the top of the list.

Usually, emissions per inhabitant are proportional to earnings. The emissions of the wealthy are very high in all countries.

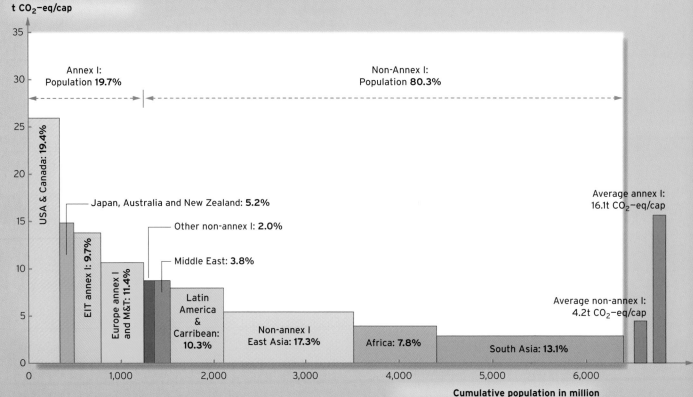

t CO_2-eq/cap

Annex I:
Population **19.7%**

Non-Annex I:
Population **80.3%**

USA & Canada: **19.4%**

Japan, Australia and New Zealand: **5.2%**

Other non-annex I: **2.0%**

Middle East: **3.8%**

EIT annex I: **9.7%**

Europe annex I and M&T: **11.4%**

Latin America & Carribean: **10.3%**

Non-annex I East Asia: **17.3%**

Africa: **7.8%**

South Asia: **13.1%**

Average annex I:
16.1t CO_2-eq/cap

Average non-annex I:
4.2t CO_2-eq/cap

Cumulative population in million

THE WORLD FROM THE POINT OF VIEW OF CO$_2$

In this representation, the size of each country has been adjusted according to its greenhouse gas emissions: this process is known as anamorphosis. The difference between the amount of emissions in the northern hemisphere and the southern hemisphere – especially in Africa – is obvious.

Chan Shan, *Beijing, China*
Everyone knows something about the environment. However, most people think of their own interests first. Actually, when people talk about the environment they are completely reasonable, but when it comes to taking action, there's a big difference.

Chan Shan

Peter

Dominic

Dominic, *California, United States*
We must change the way we live. Especially in the United States, where we believe that the more we consume, the happier we are. We cannot buy so much, and use up so much packaging and resources without expecting the other six billion people on Earth to want exactly the same thing.

Peter, *California, United States*
Well, I think as an individual I'm willing and able to do what's necessary to prevent severe events from occurring. But individual actions, as critical as they are, aren't going to be enough. They're going to have to be accompanied by community action, national action and global action.

James, *Beijing, China*
If I invited you to my home, would you damage my furniture? Would you break my lamps or my faucets? You could do it, but I don't think you'd be invited again. We are doing exactly the same to our world. If we take out the sun from the sky, if we damage the clouds above us, we might not be invited again either.

James

TAKING ACTION

Aghatam, *Bamako, Mali*
What makes me angriest is when you tell people that their behaviour can have a negative impact on the future generations and they answer: 'No, you know, God will take care of us, God will take care of the next generation.' And they don't acknowledge that God gave us intelligence, the tools to evolve, to feed ourselves, to shelter ourselves. And God did tell us to do well with what we were given. When people say things like that, I tell myself that they just don't want to change.

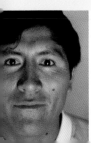

Aghatam

AN INCONVENIENT TRUTH

Why are we not doing anything, or so little? The majority of scientists are in agreement and the scenarios are bleak – some more than others. The title of the documentary on climate change featuring Al Gore is apt: *An Inconvenient Truth*. Is it so inconvenient that we refuse to see it?

The comparison is striking: we spend billions to prevent a flu pandemic, we plan emergency measures and we form crisis teams. However, we are finding it difficult to act when it comes to the environment. Yet, a climate crisis is just as likely to occur as a pandemic. The flu seems closer, as it could be here tomorrow, but the most serious consequences of global warming will only be felt the day after tomorrow. The flu affects people close to us and global warming affects those further away. We know one simple way of curing the flu, even if this cure is not perfect. It strikes suddenly, not gradually. It is caused by an enemy – a virus – while global warming is our own doing.

> ALTHOUGH HUMAN CATASTROPHES MUST BE AVOIDED AT ALL COSTS, THEY SEEM TO BE THE ONLY THING THAT TRIGGERS AN APPROPRIATE RESPONSE TO A POTENTIAL THREAT.

Despite the efforts of scientists, activists, international organisations and journalists, global warming is not as much a part of consciousness as it should be. It seems that the human mind has difficulty believing what it knows.

Because of this, some environmentalists are relying on the 'learning from disasters' argument. The Seveso disaster had to happen before laws against dioxins were passed, a heat wave had to occur before hospital services were suitably equipped, four thousand people had to die because of smog in London before the first British law on air quality was passed. Although human catastrophes must be avoided at all costs, they seem to be the only thing that triggers an appropriate response to a potential threat. Some environmentalists claim that 'the very thing that is threatening us could save us'. Let us prove them wrong for once and anticipate the forthcoming crisis.

See also pages 18, 164 and 180.

Pripiat, abandoned town near the Chernobyl nuclear power station, Ukraine (51°24'N, 30°02'E). In April 1986 in the Ukraine, the explosion of one of the Chernobyl power station's reactors caused the biggest civil nuclear disaster of all time. The exact number of victims is still not known, but it is estimated that several million people are suffering from malformations, cancer and other illnesses linked to radiation.

COLLAPSE

Sooner or later, civilizations disappear and are replaced by others. What can we learn from the ones that came before us, just before the onset of the forthcoming climate crisis? A widely researched example is Easter Island, in the Pacific Ocean. Its inhabitants' thriving culture suddenly disappeared around the year 1500 and its population decreased five-fold over the course of a single century.

According to the American scientist Jared Diamond, the reason for this could be linked to the fact that its inhabitants cut down all the trees on their island. Without trees, they could no longer build boats to fish and, more importantly, their soil eroded. As the crisis gradually worsened, the island's inhabitants waged protracted wars. In a bid to outdo each other on a religious scale, they built ever larger statues and had to cut down even more trees to move the monoliths. It was a vicious cycle.

Jared Diamond has studied other civilizations that

THE HISTORIAN ARNOLD TOYNBEE WROTE THAT 'CIVILIZATIONS DIE FROM SUICIDE, NOT MURDER.'

collapsed primarily because of the environment: the Mayas and the Babylonians overexploited their soil, while Greenland's Vikings were unable to adapt to cooling. Although there were various factors that led to the collapse of these societies, environmental crises played a major role in weakening the economic and social foundations. This pattern could certainly re-emerge today.

From a historian's point of view, the pattern of a collapse falls clearly into place. But for political, religious and social reasons, a society cannot react and take the necessary steps to ensure its survival. What did the Easter Islander who cut down the last tree think? Another prominent comparative history expert, the British historian Arnold Toynbee, wrote that 'civilizations die from suicide, not murder'. This means that they collapse because they cannot overcome their own internal crises.

See also pages 28, 144 and 162.

Tar deposits in a basin after the extraction of Athabasca oil sands, Fort MacMurray, Canada (57°01'N, 111°38'W). Oil sands have been exploited for about thirty years and represent the second largest petrol reserve in the world, with an estimated potential of 173 million barrels. But to obtain one barrel - 159 litres - four tons of peat, soil and sand have to be extracted. The process also produces residual pollutants.

THE MONTREAL PROTOCOL

It is possible to reach an agreement on the climate rapidly. The negotiations that led to the Montreal Protocol in 1987 showed this to be true. The aim of this protocol was to reduce and eventually eliminate substances that impoverish the ozone layer.

In 1985, scientists raised the alarm: the ozone layer above Antarctica had become dangerously thin – a 'hole' had appeared. Ozone blocks the sun's harmful ultraviolet rays. Without this fine layer of gas, almost no life on Earth would be possible. After scientific data began rapidly accumulating, proving that the hole was getting larger, representatives from the main industrial countries consulted each other. Barely two years later in 1987, twenty-four countries met in Canada and adopted the Montreal Protocol. It sought to eliminate the production of substances that deplete the ozone layer: gases used as refrigerants and propellants, chlorofluorocarbons (CFCs) and hydrochlorofluorocarbons (HCFCs). The protocol has since been adopted by 191 countries and thanks to this treaty, the ozone layer could return to a normal level by 2055.

HOW COME THE MONTREAL PROTOCOL MET WITH IMMEDIATE APPROVAL WHILE THE KYOTO PROTOCOL IS STILL BEING DEBATED?

How come the Montreal Protocol met with immediate approval while the Kyoto Protocol is still being debated? The first reason is that the threat posed by the weakening ozone layer was clear: the disappearance of humankind. The findings were unanimous. In comparison, the consequences of global warming are more complex and controversial. The second reason is that substances were available to replace CFCs and HCFCs. Conversely, our societies still depend on hydrocarbons and, for the moment, there is no simple way to replace them on a large scale. However, as time goes by, the effects of global warming will become more prominent and the alternatives will become feasible.

See also pages 28, 130 and 142.

Ushuaia, Argentina (54°47'S, 68°18'W). Ushuaia is at the southernmost tip of South America in the province of Tierra del Fuego. It has around fifty thousand inhabitants, who live off of naval construction, forest exploitation, fishing and tourism. The hole in the ozone layer means that this community, which is particularly exposed to the sun, must take extra care to protect themselves from ultraviolet rays.

MONEY MATTERS

Inaction is a luxury that we can no longer afford. It is a luxury because global warming has already started to change our planet and will continue to do so. This is going to be extremely expensive.

Insurance companies were the first to identify the phenomenon: as the years passed, they began to notice an increase in the number of claims they received that were related to natural disasters like Hurricane Katrina, the European heat waves of 2003 and recurrent floods in Central Europe and Asia. Experts have since tried to fully evaluate the phenomenon. According to Nicholas Stern, previously an economic advisor for the British government, global warming will cost about 5 per cent of the world GDP today and in coming years. If we take a wider range of risks and consequences into account, the damage reaches up to 20 per cent of the world GDP. This is the equivalent of five trillion dollars, or the combined cost of the two world wars plus the Great Depression.

THE DAMAGE REACHES UP TO 20 PER CENT OF THE WORLD GDP. THIS IS THE EQUIVALENT OF FIVE TRILLION DOLLARS, OR THE COMBINED COST OF THE TWO WORLD WARS PLUS THE GREAT DEPRESSION.

And yet, according to Stern, preventive measures are ten to twenty times less expensive. It seems like a no-brainer. Even if the current crisis is taking a toll on the economy, the investments we need to make in order to reorient our society will be profitable. Moreover, the longer we wait to act, the more the situation will become difficult, the more the necessary steps will be restrictive and the more it will cost. According to experts, we have about ten years to act. After that, it will be very difficult to turn things around.

We can take action. But new methods to make decisions and share the effort have to be found, as the current system has not managed to do this. As Stern wrote: 'Climate change presents a unique challenge for economics: it is the greatest and widest-ranging market failure ever seen'.

See also pages 84, 162 and 172.

Mechanical diggers stored in the Yokohama port, Japan (35°28'N, 139°39'E). Hundreds of industrial machines are lined up on a wharf, ready to be exported. Yokohama, south of Tokyo, is the country's second-largest city with 3.6 million inhabitants. The port is the centre of Japanese trade: every year, 100 billion euros of merchandise is exchanged here.

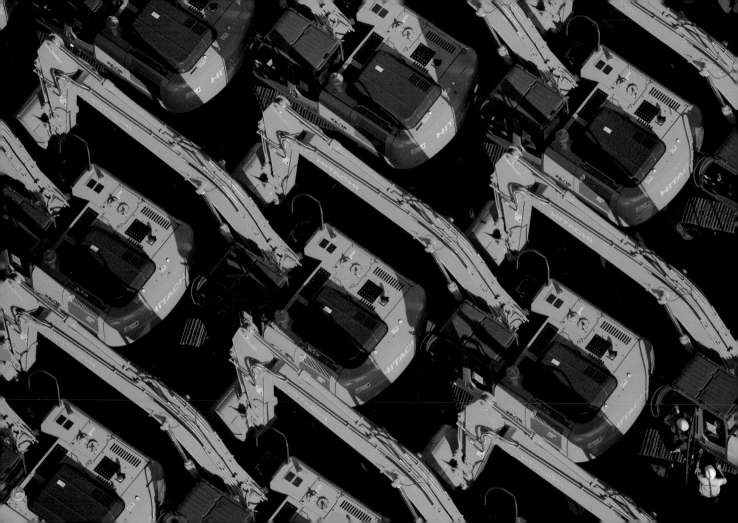

CONSUMING RESPONSIBLY

The Drax Power Station in the United Kingdom is the country's most pollutive power station: it emits almost twenty-two million tons of CO_2 a year. This is 2.5 million times more than an ordinary British citizen. In light of this, individual efforts to limit your own emissions can seem laughable.

From a moral point of view, just because others are doing the wrong thing doesn't make it okay, nor does it mean that we shouldn't all try to do our best. But from a practical point of view, people still use a lot of electricity to light their homes, for example, or even indirectly for street lights or to do business. Drax produces 7 per cent of the UK's electricity. This is the equivalent of what four million people consume.

Companies that control Drax or other industrial sites earn money by selling polluting energy, but they can only do so because others are prepared to buy it. Consumers have seized political power before, when

> CITIZENS ARE NOT THE ONLY ONES WHO MUST MAKE AN EFFORT; GOVERNMENTS ALSO HAVE A ROLE TO PLAY AND CAN INCREASE THE EFFICIENCY OF INITIATIVES.

Gandhi organized the boycott of British goods (in the 1920s), during the boycott of racially segregated buses in the United States in 1955, and, more recently, against companies like Shell and Nike. Over the past few decades, this sort of action has developed further because of fair and responsible trade.

Citizens are not the only ones who must make an effort; governments also have a role to play and can increase the efficiency of initiatives. The best example is the EU Energy Label. This label, which has been compulsory for certain domestic electrical appliances in the European Union since 1995, is based on a set of energy efficiency classes from A to G. In the space of a few years, it has significantly changed the market and consumption patterns.

See also pages 172, 178 and 184.

Cotton fabric drying in the sun in Sanganer, Rajasthan, India (26°49'N, 75°47'E). Rajasthan is a major textile production centre and is known for dyeing and imprinting cotton and silk. These handmade products, extremely popular with tourists, are produced by women. Indian women bear the brunt of the country's poverty, which affects 25 per cent of the population.

GREEN BUSINESS AND GREENWASHING

Ecology and the economy are not necessarily contradictory. The world market of eco-products and services has already reached $1.37 trillion a year. This figure could increase to $2.74 trillion by 2020. Within the European Union, thirty-one million jobs are already related to the environment.

One can make money by being green. This is the idea behind what is known as green business or, alternately, the green economy. The idea is to produce and install wind turbines, energy-saving equipment, and so on, as well as doing what we used to do before in a different way. Within each company, an approach that considers the environment makes it possible to reduce costs through eco-conception, reducing transport, and energy and raw material needs.

But beware of greenwashing. This occurs when a environmental cause is used to embellish something – a brand, company or product – that is not really eco-friendly. For example, between 2006 and 2007, the number of green adverts almost tripled in France. Some even claimed that SUVs that polluted slightly less than others were green. Of course, we must not forget that any company's primary aim is to make money. For some companies, it is not in their interest to change their practices and they will only do so if forced by law, for example.

Like the industrial revolution and the information technology revolution, there could also be an environmental revolution in industry. Looms have been mechanized; typewriters have been replaced by computers. Urban SUVs could be replaced by electrically powered vehicles. Some sectors of the economy might suffer, but others will gain. Switching to a greener economy might create more jobs than it will suppress.

See also pages 138, 168 and 176.

> ECOLOGY AND THE ECONOMY ARE NOT NECESSARILY CONTRADICTORY. THE WORLD MARKET OF ECO-PRODUCTS AND SERVICES HAS ALREADY REACHED $1.37 TRILLION A YEAR.

Tiergarten, Berlin, Germany (52°30'N, 13°22'E). Once the weather gets nice, Berliners hop on their bikes to cycle through this large park in the capital. In big cities today, a car doesn't go any faster than a horse-drawn carriage did a century ago. Bicycles, which are cheap, quiet and don't pollute, take up six times less road space than cars. When parked, they take up twenty times less space. Air pollution linked to transportation is responsible for three million deaths a year around the world.

CARBON OFFSETTING

When it's not possible to reduce your greenhouse gas emissions, you can offset them. This means supporting a project that absorbs an amount of carbon equal to your emissions. Planting trees to offset the emissions of a plane trip is the most common technique. This voluntary practice should not be mistaken for the industrial conformity compensation, which is part of a regulatory framework.

Today, the voluntary carbon offset mechanism is within the reach of everyone. Almost 150 operators (including GoodPlanet and its *Action Carbone* program) offer solutions; this practice is becoming increasingly popular. In 2008, 123 million carbon credits (the equivalent number of tons in carbon) were purchased in Western countries. However, this type of compensation is still not that common: it only accounts for 0.3 per cent of global emissions. **The variety and the young age of those involved explains why people sometimes doubt the seriousness of the sector.** Today, there are several standards to ensure certain criteria have been met. These include additionality, which means that CO_2 reductions would not have been possible without the consumer's paying for them; measurability, which means that emissions have to be estimated accurately; and permanence, which means that CO_2 reductions have to be sustainable. Some projects also have an economic and social dimension by helping the development of local communities.

Carbon compensation should go hand in hand with a real effort to reduce your emissions. Without this, it is just a guilt-free way of continuing to emit greenhouse gases. This is why some see carbon offsetting as an indulgence. The misuse of this practice – the remission of one's sins for money (or pious actions) – was heavily criticized in the Middle Ages. Sometimes, voluntary compensation is more of a way of making people aware of the issues surrounding global warming rather than solving them.

See also pages 34, 140 and 170.

> CARBON COMPENSATION
> SHOULD GO HAND IN HAND
> WITH A REAL EFFORT
> TO REDUCE YOUR EMISSIONS.

Tourist resort in Sitio de Calahonda, Spain (36°30'N, 4°42'W). Calahonda is located on the Costa del Sol, a few kilometres east of Marbella, and attracts many foreign tourists every year. Mass tourism disfigures landscapes and disturbs ecosystems. It is also responsible for a large amount of greenhouse gas emissions because of the increasing number of international journeys.

CARBON TAX

Tobacco and alcohol are both taxed. Why can't we do the same thing for carbon? For the first two, the tax covers the related social and medical costs. The point of a carbon tax would be to cover the environmental cost of greenhouse gases. Putting a price on pollution would encourage everyone to reduce emissions. Additionally, it would allow governments to collect money to fund clean energy and prepare for the future. A twenty dollar tax for every ton of carbon emitted would raise 265 billion dollars a year in OECD countries.

In Denmark, the introduction of a carbon tax led to a 6 per cent decrease in CO$_2$ emissions between 1988 and 1997 while the economic growth rate was at 20 per cent. In 1997, the level of this tax was increased, leading to a 5 per cent reduction over the course of a year. Several countries are now considering taking similar measures.

The concrete details of setting up a carbon tax are complex. Who will have to pay? What will it cover? The polluter-payer principle could be applied. This would mean that each person who emits greenhouse gases would have to pay a tax depending on his or her emissions. But should emissions be targeted at the source or once the product is finished? How can we calculate the energy consumption or the carbon impact caused by producing and transporting products? And how can we prevent the tax from crippling the poor?

The application of such a tax to international trade has even been considered: it would apply to products from countries which don't enforce the Kyoto Protocol or countries that aren't taking any steps to fight global warming. Such a system would be advantageous because it would fight against environmental dumping, but it would be very hard to put into place. It could also wind up resembling protectionism, which is against WTO regulations.

See also pages 34, 138 and 152.

BUT SHOULD EMISSIONS BE TARGETED AT THE SOURCE OR ONCE THE PRODUCT IS FINISHED? HOW CAN WE CALCULATE THE ENERGY CONSUMPTION OR THE CARBON IMPACT CAUSED BY PRODUCING AND TRANSPORTING PRODUCTS?

Scrap yard, Saint-Brieuc, Côtes-d'Armor, France (48°31'N, 2°46'W). These cars have been crushed and stacked onto one another, awaiting removal. A car's impact is mainly linked to how it is used. According to the World Health Organisation, 1.2 million people around the world die in car accidents every year. And transport - mainly on roads - is responsible for about 20 per cent of total greenhouse gas emissions.

EAT LESS MEAT

Reducing the amount of meat you eat is the simplest, most effective step you can take to reduce your greenhouse gas emissions. Animal husbandry, both directly and indirectly, accounts for almost 18 per cent of greenhouse gas emissions. This is more than transportation.

The expansion of cattle ranching is one of the main causes of deforestation. Space is needed for animals to graze, which is often taken from the forest. Additionally, feeding the animals in intensive stockbreeding requires large amounts of food: it takes seven kilos of soybeans or corn, thirty-six kilos of fodder and sixteen thousand litres of water to produce one kilo of beef. Soybean crops are primarily grown on land that has been taken from the Amazon forest. Deforestation emits large amounts of greenhouse gas.

Moreover, cows release methane, a powerful greenhouse gas, through flatulence and belching - it adds up to almost one hundred litres a day per animal! You also have

> ## ONE KILO OF BEEF IS THE EQUIVALENT OF EIGHTEEN KILOS OF CO_2 – AS MUCH CARBON AS A CAR EMITS OVER ONE HUNDRED KILOMETRES!

to take into account the CO_2 emissions produced by transporting the food to the consumer over thousands of kilometres. In total, one kilo of beef is the equivalent of eighteen kilos of CO_2 - as much carbon as a car emits over one hundred kilometres! On a global average, each person consumes forty kilos of meat a year (eighty-three kilos in developed countries compared to thirty-one kilos in developing countries). This is double the amount that was consumed fifty years ago.

Rajendra Pachauri, the president of the IPCC, has thus advised, 'Start by giving up meat one day a week and cut down gradually'. You can start by transitioning from red meat to white meat, which is responsible for five to ten times less greenhouse gas emissions. Poultry do not emit any methane and, above all, require much less energy to be raised. They are slaughtered at a much younger age. And of course, there are the terrible conditions in which livestock are kept.

See also pages 46, 108 and 170.

Bovine feedlot near Young, Rio Negro, Uruguay (32°42'S, 57°38'W). In recent years, intensive animal husbandry based has developed significantly. Feedlots make it possible to produce a lot of meat in a very small space, but have been criticized for ethical, environmental and health reasons. Meat from feedlots is particularly high in saturated fat.

A SEATTLE CLIMATE

During the 1999 WTO summit, demonstrations in Seattle put alter-globalization on the international agenda and influenced negotiations for years. If the Copenhagen summit causes popular involvement on such a massive scale, it could become the environmental equivalent of the Seattle protests – without the violence that occurred during the American convention, we hope.

A lot of environmental NGOs (including GoodPlanet) are planning to send representatives to Copenhagen. Some will be on-site as official observers, some will be there as delegates and some will simply be in the city's streets taking part in various activities and demonstrations. Most of them will organize events in their country before and after the summit.

However, for the moment, the environmental movement rallies a lot less people than other major issues in the West. Large trade unions can make hundreds of thousands of

THE ENVIRONMENTAL MOVEMENT RALLIES A LOT LESS PEOPLE THAN OTHER MAJOR ISSUES IN THE WEST.

people take to the streets. The movement against the 2003 war in Iraq mobilized several million protestors all around the world. In comparison, the tens of thousands of people protesting against global warming in London seemed only to be staging a performance.

As long as politicians think that climate change is not important for voters, they will put off making the necessary decisions: regardless of their personal convictions, they depend on their electors. They evaluate the state of public opinion through votes, surveys and by observing demonstrations and other popular events. This is why it is important to get everyone involved.

Of course, authoritarian regimes, like in China, do not react in the same way, even though they do consider public opinion to a certain extent. This is another reason why we should take advantage of our freedom of speech.

See also pages 162, 164 and 186.

The Acropolis, Athens, Greece (37°58′N, 23°43′E). The ancient Greeks built one of the most remarkable architectural ensembles in the history of humanity, all contained on a plateau that covers a little less than three hectares. It is now Unesco's official emblem. Four masterpieces of classical Greek art – the Parthenon, the Propylaea, the Erechtheum and the Temple of Athena Nike – exhibit the magnificence of the Athenian democracy under Pericles.

OVERPOPULATION

By the year 2012, there will be seven billion human beings on Earth. This is twice as many people as there were in the 1960s: those born after World War II are the only generation to have seen the population double within their lifetime. They are also the only ones to have simultaneously witnessed a skyrocketing GDP as well as the emerging climate threat. Population, production, pollution: the link led the biologist Paul Ehrlich to talk about the 'P bomb'. He suggested having fewer children to save the planet.

The demographic issue should be considered together with each inhabitant's ecological footprint. If the entire world lived like an American or a Dane, we would need over four planets to satisfy our needs. But by living like an Indian, half of one would be enough. Today, one billion of the richest inhabitants emit as much greenhouse gas as the rest of the world combined.

Theoretically, the planet will be able to support the nine billion people living on it in 2050. However, it will not

THE MOST EFFECTIVE WAY TO REDUCE OUR IMPACT ON THE PLANET IS TO TAKE SIMULTANEOUS ACTION ON THE POPULATION AND OUR ECOLOGICAL FOOTPRINT.

be able to support nine billion meat-eating car owners who lead Western lifestyles. The way of life that is currently held up as an example is not sustainable. It is up to rich countries to lower their consumption and suggest another development model that will be viable for the entire world.

The most effective way to reduce our impact on the planet is to take simultaneous action on the population and our ecological footprint. But controlling the population does not have to mean limiting the number of births in an authoritarian way. Making contraception available is the first step. The second, more important step is providing access to education. Globally, the fertility rate for women with a secondary education is 1.9 children compared to 4.5 children for uneducated women. School is not just a means for social and cultural development, but is also a key for environmental issues.

See also pages 62, 86 and 150.

Harvesting tea leaves, Kericho region, Kenya (0°24'S, 37°00'E). It is in Africa's Rift Valley that *Homo sapiens* are believed to have taken their first steps two hundred thousand years ago, before spreading out across the world's continents. The world population remained stable at three hundred million inhabitants for the first millennium of the Christian era, but it exploded in the last century. As of June 2009, there were 6.81 billion people on Earth.

DEGROWTH

Since the industrial era, the Western development model has been based on the increasing exploitation of natural resources, including fossil fuels. The problem is that these resources are limited and will one day run out. For some, degrowth is the answer. This concept was theorized by the economist Nicholas Georgescu-Roegen in the 1970s and has once again come to the fore because of the global economic recession. The principle is straightforward: the end of growth is unavoidable, so we need to anticipate it if we want to live well in the future.

Degrowth is a key word that brings together diverse personalities from different walks of life. It is also an implicit criticism of the idea of sustainable development which is, in fact, a contradiction since infinite growth is impossible and therefore not sustainable.

Living better with less. This is the individual form of the idea that is also called voluntary simplicity. Those who apply it try to resist being conditioned by advertising and the artificial needs it creates in our minds. Just as Greek and Asian wisdom encouraged moderation and contentment, degrowth's proponents seek inner peace. They are also seeking social equity and a smaller ecological footprint. As Gandhi used to say, 'There is enough on earth for everybody's need, but not enough for anybody's greed.'

One question remains: how can we apply degrowth to an entire society? Degrowth implies difficult and controversial changes – relocating the economy, favouring less material wealth indicators over the GDP, encouraging a culture of being rather than a culture based on possessions and appearances. Such changes would require us to reevaluate our social models and would affect the way we live. The environmental crisis has an anthropological dimension. This could mean that we might have to redefine the very meaning of the individual and collective human adventure.

See also pages 152, 164 and 170.

'THERE IS ENOUGH ON EARTH FOR EVERYBODY'S NEED, BUT NOT ENOUGH FOR ANYBODY'S GREED.'

Bottle racks near Braunschweig, Germany (52°19'N, 10°31'E). Bottles of mineral water, beer, fruit juice and soft drinks are piled up at a wholesaler's storage area. The amount of bottled water consumed worldwide increased by 70 per cent between 2002 and 2007. But producing, conditioning and transporting one bottle of water requires the equivalent of one-quarter of its contents in oil.

IT IS TOO LATE TO BE PESSIMISTIC

As Al Gore said, 'Each and every one of us can make changes in the way in which we live our lives and become part of the solution'. Fighting global warming means accepting responsibility for the planet's future and deciding to act conscientiously in all areas of your life. We each have to find our own way of doing this, which is why there is no one single method. There are as many solutions as there are ways to tackle the problem.

You can significantly reduce your greenhouse gas emissions by choosing to eat less meat or consuming responsibly, for example. You can share your ideas by talking with acquaintances or on the internet. You can also increase your ability to influence the outcome by taking collective action, joining an environmental organization or voting for candidates for whom fighting global warming is a priority.

Obviously, a lot of individual actions only take on meaning in a larger setting. City councils organize collective transport, for example. Governments can forbid incandescent light bulbs or grant tax credits for renewable energy. On an international level, many agreements regarding the climate, pesticides, the ozone layer and so on have been signed over the past few years. In most cases, individual action has inspired and influenced legislators and politicians.

IPCC scientists have given us several reasons to act. If we don't, the planet's ecological balance could become disrupted. Economists have given us another reason: global warming will be expensive. Taking the necessary action now will not only allow us to save money, but will even provide us with new business opportunities. But there is also a moral component: we should consider the world that we will leave behind for our children and their children. Finally, there are also personal reasons: taking action will make you happy. Just try it and see.

TAKING ACTION WILL MAKE YOU HAPPY. JUST TRY IT AND SEE.

Stocking white sweet corn, the edge of the Masai Mara National Reserve, Kenya (1°30'S, 35°10'E). White corn is one of the staple foods in Africa. It is much more popular than yellow corn which is used primarily for fodder. In Africa, white corn accounts for almost a quarter of total agricultural production. This is why its cultivation is important for the continent's food security.

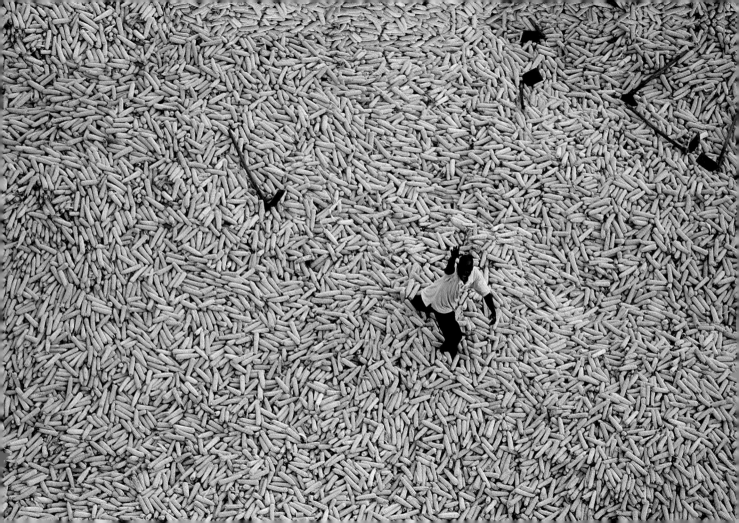

INDEX

The headings and numbers in bold refer to subjects that are the theme of an entire page. The numbers in italics indicate photograph captions.

PHOTOGRAPHS

All of the photographs in this title (including the cover) were taken by Yann Arthus-Bertrand, except for the portraits at the beginning of each section, which were used by permission of the project *6 billion Others*.
All of Yann Arthus-Bertrand's photographs were provided by the Altitude Agency, Paris, France.

MAPS AND GRAPHICS

The diagrams in this book are adapted from Intergovernmental Panel on Climate Change (IPCC) documents, especially the following:

Climate Change 2007: Synthesis Report. Contribution of Working Groups I, II and III to the *Fourth Assessment Report of the Intergovernmental Panel on Climate Change* for pages 30, 31, 58, 59, 88, 126, 158. IPCC, Geneva, Switzerland. *Climate Change 2007: Impacts, Adaptation and Vulnerability*. Working Group II Contribution to the *Fourth Assessment Report of the Intergovernmental Panel on Climate Change* for page 89. Cambridge University Press. *Climate Change 2007: Mitigation of Climate Change*. Working Group III Contribution to the Fourth Assessment Report of the Intergovernmental Panel on Climate Change. Cambridge University Press for page 127.
The map on page 159 is copyright of the SASI Group (University of Sheffield) and Mark Newman (University of Michigan).

COPYRIGHT

This publication can be reproduced in any form, in its entirety or as an extract, with no modifications, for educational or nonprofit purposes without prior permission of the copyright holder, as long as the source is acknowledged. All text is copyright of Creative Commons (BY - NC - SA).

DISCLAIMER

While the utmost care has been taken to ensure that the content of this publication is factually correct and appropriately referenced, GoodPlanet does not accept any responsibility for the accuracy and exhaustiveness of the content. It is not in any way liable for any direct or indirect loss or damage resulting from the use of the content of this publication or for any confidence placed in its content.

This book is printed on Satimat Green 170 g/m^2 coated paper made out of 60% recycled fibres, 40% virgin FSC fibres.
Satimat is a product and registered trademark of the Arjowiggings Group.
Thanks to its high recycled-fibre content, the impact of the production of this ecoconceived paper on natural resources (water, energy and wood) was reduced.

Abrams books are available at special discounts when purchased in quantity for premiums and promotions as well as fundraising or educational use. Special editions can also be created to specification. For details, contact specialmarkets@hnabooks.com or the adress below.

Photo-engraving: Quadrilaser
Printed by Mame en France
ISBN: 978-0-8109-9578-9

115 West 18th Street
New York, NY 10011
www.abramsbooks.com